OXFORD

7

Maths Links

Ray Allan

Martin Williams

Practice Book

Great Clarendon Street, Oxford OX2 6DP

Oxford University Press is a department of the University of Oxford. It furthers the University's objective of excellence in research, scholarship, and education by publishing worldwide in

Oxford New York

Auckland Cape Town Dar es Salaam Hong Kong Karachi Kuala Lumpur Madrid Melbourne Mexico City Nairobi New Delhi Shanghai Taipei Toronto

With offices in

Argentina Austria Brazil Chile Czech Republic France Greece Guatemala Hungary Italy Japan Poland Portugal Singapore South Korea Switzerland Thailand Turkey Ukraine Vietnam

First published 2008

British Library Cataloguing in Publication Data

Data available

ISBN-13: 9780-19-915282-7
10 9 8 7 6 5 4 3 2 1

Printed in Great Britain by Ashford Colour Press Ltd.

Paper used in the production of this book is a natural, recyclable product made from wood grown in sustainable forests. The manufacturing process conforms to the environmental regulations to the country of origin.

Acknowledgements
The editors would like to thank Kim Fraser for her outstanding work on this book.

1b Place value

I can do this page!

1 What does the circled digit stand for in each number?

a 1(8)5 — 8 tens or eighty

b (5)7

c 21(5)

d (1)892

e 1(5)20

2 Here are three digits: 

a What is the smallest number you can make? 

b What is the largest number you can make? 

3 What numbers are shown here?

a 

____

b 100 | 100 | 100 | 10 | 10 | 1 | 1 ________

c 100 | 100 | 100 | 10 | 1 | 1 | 1 ________

4 Write these numbers as 100s, 10s and units on the cards like question 3.

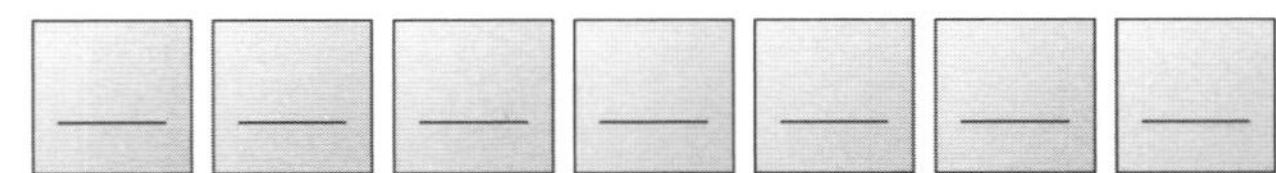

c 420 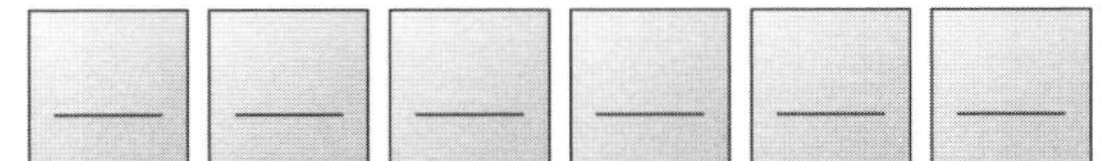

d 205 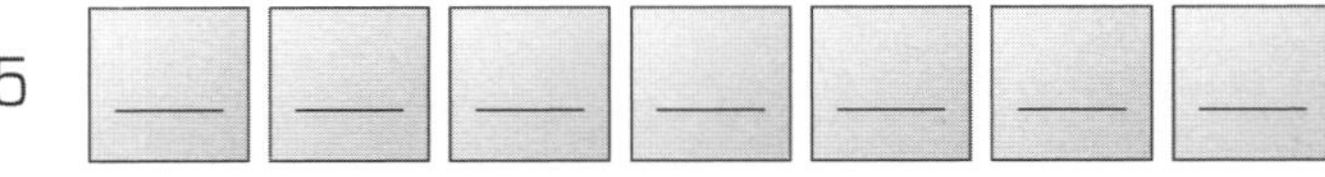

I can do this page!

1c Temperature

1 On this number line the arrow points to position 9.

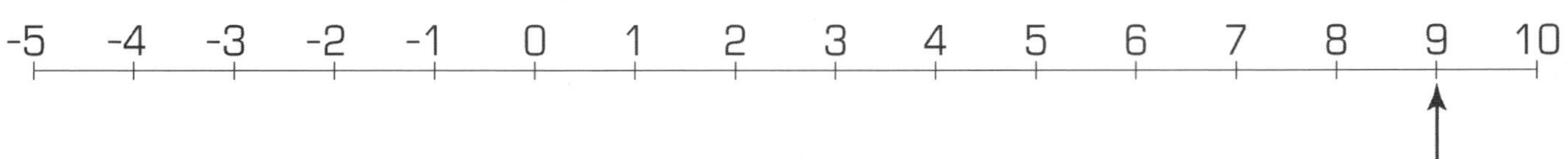

Draw arrows to point to these positions.

Label the arrows with their letters.

a 5 **b** -3 **c** -1 **d** 8 **e** 0

2 Thermometers measure temperature.

Write the missing temperatures on these thermometers.

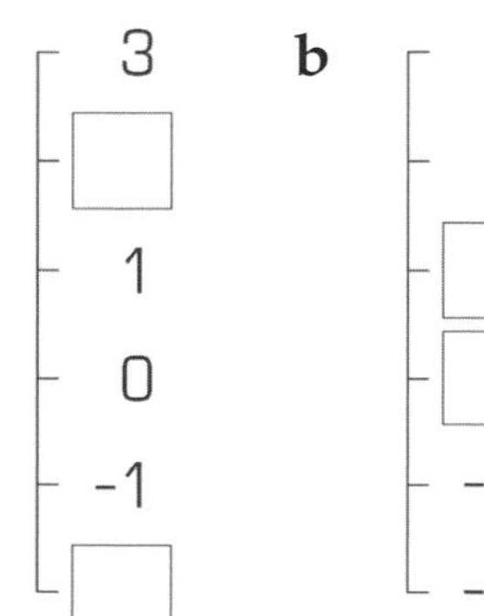

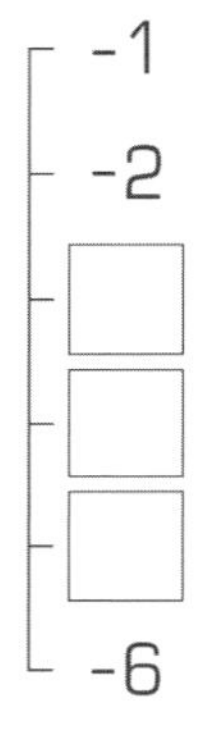

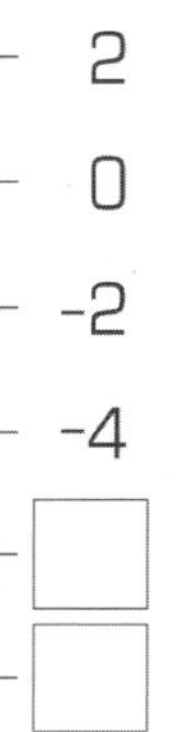

3 Circle the lower temperature in each pair.

a -3 °C 4 °C

b 2 °C 4 °C

c 6 °C 0 °C

d 3 °C -1 °C

e -1 °C 1 °C

f 5 °C -5 °C

4 Complete this number line that starts at -10.

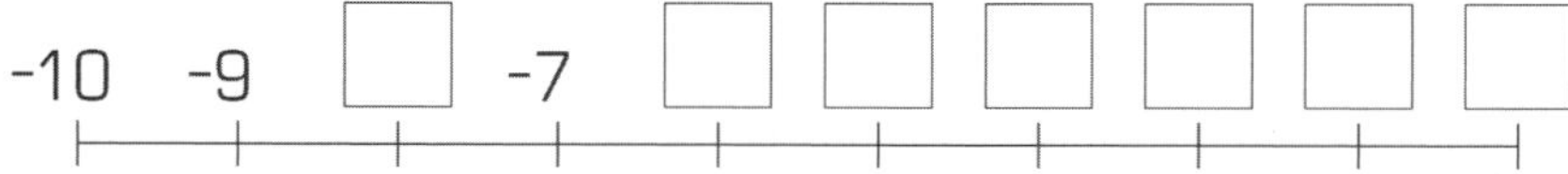

1d Mental addition

Use these number lines to help you add these numbers.

The first one is done for you.

1 13 + 14 = 27

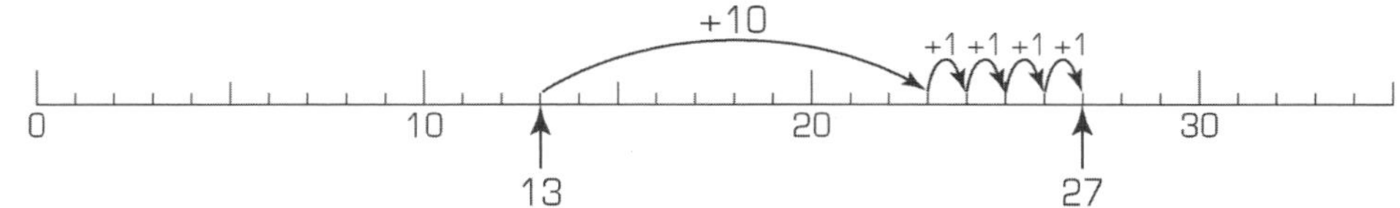

2 20 + 8 = ______

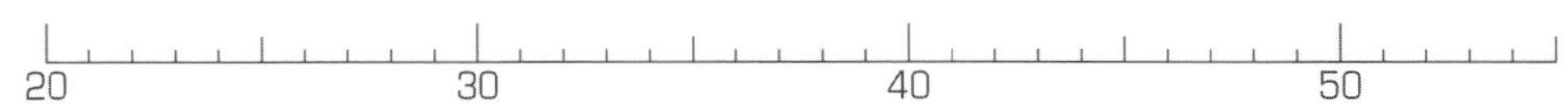

3 50 + 18 = ______

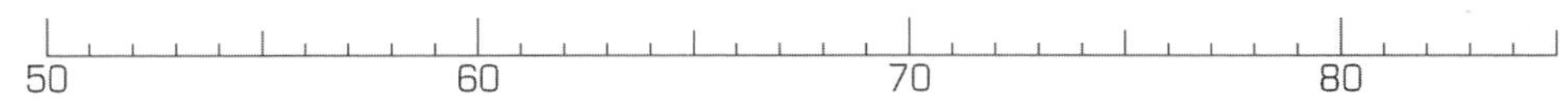

4 40 + 29 = ______

5 23 + 20 = ______

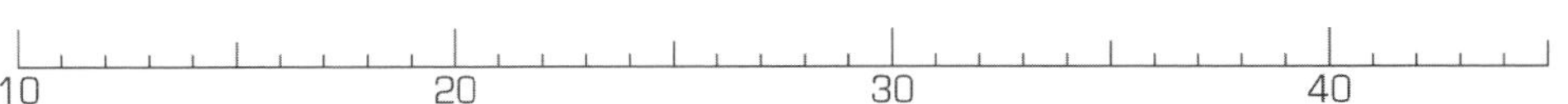

6 10 + 19 = ______

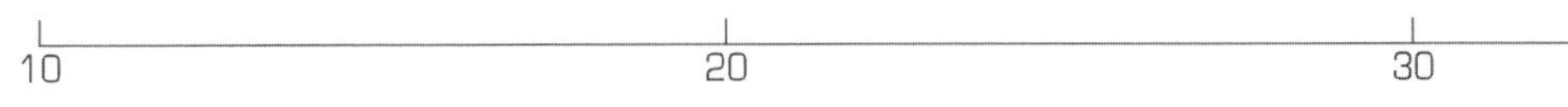

7 40 + 32 = ______

40 50 60 70 80

8 26 + 33 = ______

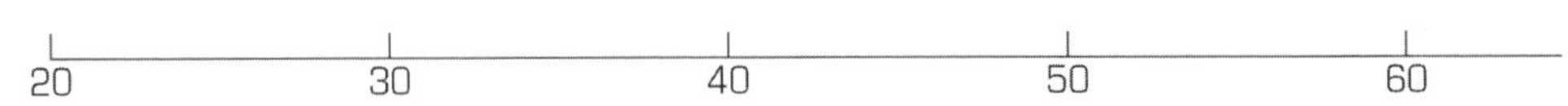

9 11 + 29 = ______

1e Mental subtraction

I can do this page!

1 Circle the largest number in each box.

Find the difference between the numbers.

a 8 (12) Difference = 4	**b** 9 15 Difference = ____	**c** 11 7 Difference = ____
d 13 9 Difference = ____	**e** 14 7 Difference = ____	**f** 7 13 Difference = ____
g 9 15 Difference = ____	**h** 16 8 Difference = ____	**i** 4 10 Difference = ____
j 13 8 Difference = ____	**k** 16 7 Difference = ____	**l** 6 11 Difference = ____

2 Subtract these numbers.

a 14 − 10 = ____ **b** 16 − 10 = ____ **c** 13 − 10 = ____

d 17 − 10 = ____ **e** 11 − 10 = ____ **f** 15 − 10 = ____

g 12 − 10 = ____ **h** 18 − 10 = ____ **i** 15 − 5 = ____

j 13 − 3 = ____ **k** 17 − 7 = ____ **l** 12 − 2 = ____

m 19 − 9 = ____ **n** 14 − 4 = ____ **o** 11 − 1 = ____

2a Sequences

1 Here is a pattern that grows. Complete the last two parts of this pattern.

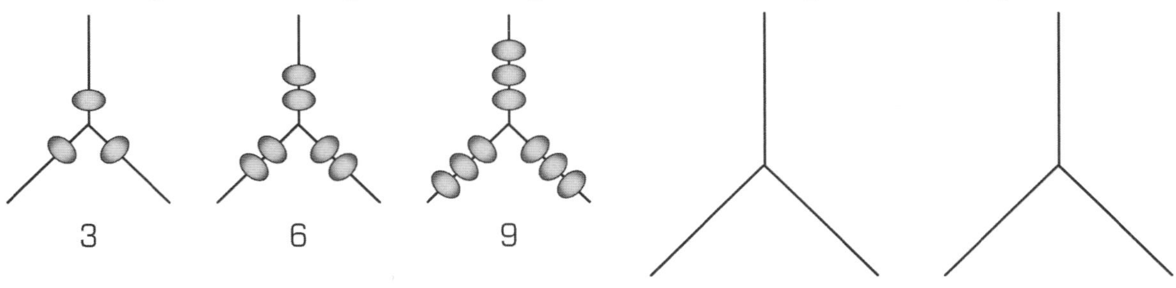

2 Each set of cards shows a number pattern.

Complete the pattern.

3 This drawing shows 1 table and 5 chairs:

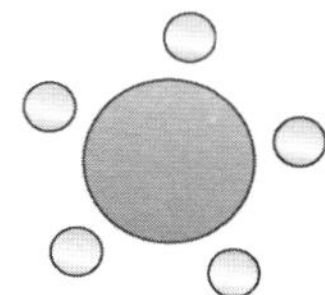

a Complete the third drawing in this sequence:

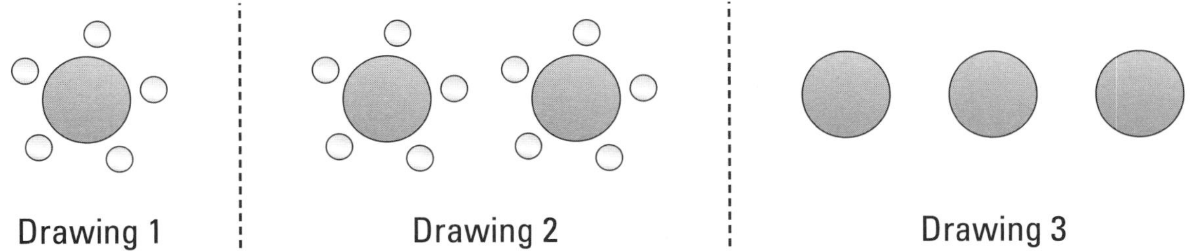

b Complete this sentence: 'Each table has ____ chairs'.

4 a Add the next drawing in this sequence

b Complete this sentence: 'Each square uses ____ matches'.

2b Describing sequences

I can do this page!

1 Write the next number in each **sequence** in the box.

a

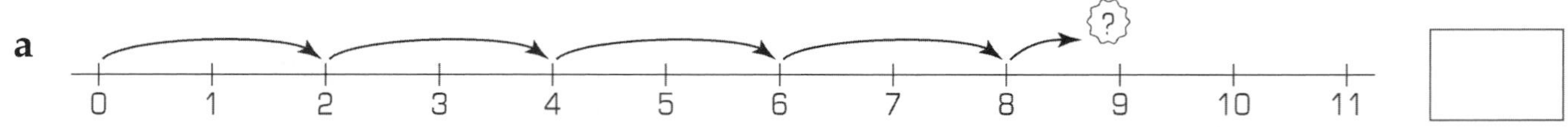

b

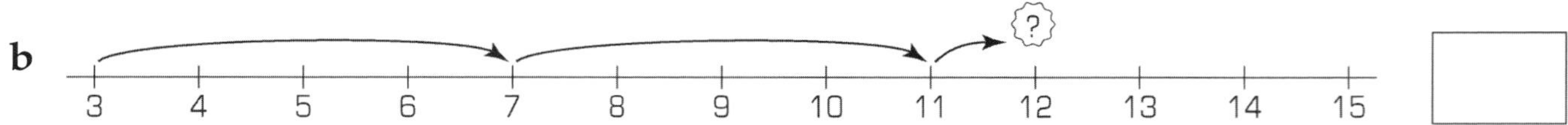

c

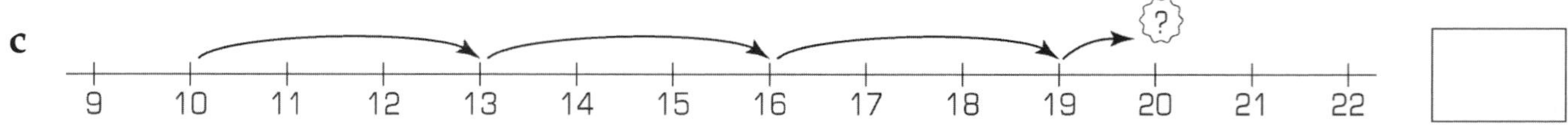

2 Complete each sequence and describe the pattern.

Here are some words to help you.

> This sequence starts at _____.
>
> This sequence increases by _____ each time.
>
> This sequence decreases by _____ each time.

a 1, 4, 7, 10, _____, _____ This sequence ______________________

b 10, 20, 30, 40, _____, _____ This sequence ______________________

c 0, 4, 8, 12, _____, _____ This sequence ______________________

d 3, 8, 13, 18, _____, _____ This sequence ______________________

e 24, 21, 18, 15, _____, _____ This sequence ______________________

3 The **rule** of a sequence tells you how to get to the next number.

Use the **rule** to write the first five numbers in each sequence.

a Start at 0. The rule is +3. _____, _____, _____, _____, _____

b Start at 2. The rule is +2. _____, _____, _____, _____, _____

c Start at 7. The rule is +5. _____, _____, _____, _____, _____

2c Using rules

1 Start at the bottom and follow the sequence to work out who is who!

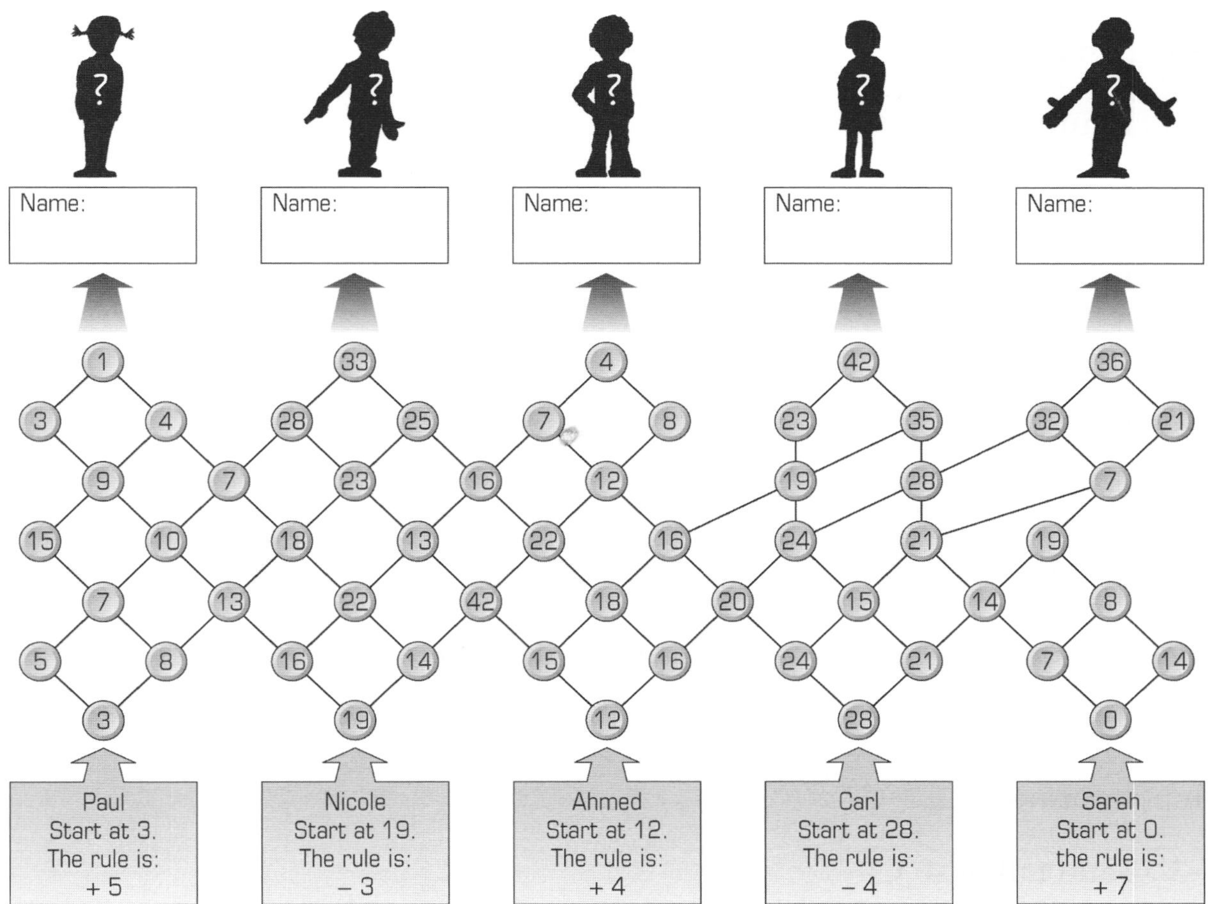

a Write the sequence for Paul. ______, ______, ______, ______, ______ ______, ______

b Write the sequence for Nicole. ______, ______, ______, ______, ______ ______, ______

c Write the sequence for Ahmed. ______, ______, ______, ______, ______ ______, ______

d Write the sequence for Carl. ______, ______, ______, ______, ______ ______, ______

e Write the sequence for Sarah. ______, ______, ______, ______, ______ ______, ______

2 Write the start number and rule for each sequence.

a 5, 7, 9, 11, 13, 15, … Start at ______ The rule is ____________________.

b 2, 7, 12, 17, 22, 27, … Start at ______ The rule is ____________________.

c 20, 18, 16, 14, 12, 10, … Start at ______ The rule is ____________________.

d 20, 30, 40, 50, 60, 70, … Start at ______ The rule is ____________________.

2d Sequences with negative numbers

1 Find the final temperature. Use the thermometer to help you.

a Start at -5 °C and rise by 7 °C

Final temperature = _____ °C

b Start at -3 °C and rise by 5 °C

Final temperature = _____ °C

c Start at -4 °C and rise by 8 °C

Final temperature = _____ °C

d Start at -7 °C and rise by 5 °C

Final temperature = _____ °C

2 Final the final temperature. Use the thermometer to help you.

a Start at -5 °C and fall by 3 °C

Final temperature = _____ °C

b Start at -3 °C and fall by 4 °C

Final temperature = _____ °C

c Start at -1 °C and fall by 8 °C

Final temperature = _____ °C

d Start at -2 °C and fall by 6 °C

Final temperature = _____ °C

3 Fill in the missing numbers from these sequences.

a Start at -8 and add 3.

-8, -5, _____, 1, _____, _____, 10, _____

b Start at 5 and subtract 2.

5, _____, _____, -1, _____, -5, _____

2e Functions

1 Work out these calculations

a 2 + 5 = ______	**b** 9 − 3 = ______	**c** 10 × 2 = ______
d 15 ÷ 3 = ______	**e** 12 − 4 = ______	**f** 16 ÷ 4 = ______
g 4 × 10 = ______	**h** 6 + 12 = ______	**i** 20 ÷ 5 = ______
j 30 + 50 = ______	**k** 5 + 27 = ______	**l** 38 − 4 = ______
m 22 − 15 = ______	**n** 2 × 8 = ______	**o** 24 ÷ 4 = ______

2 In this machine:

The function is + 5.

The input is 4   The output is 9.

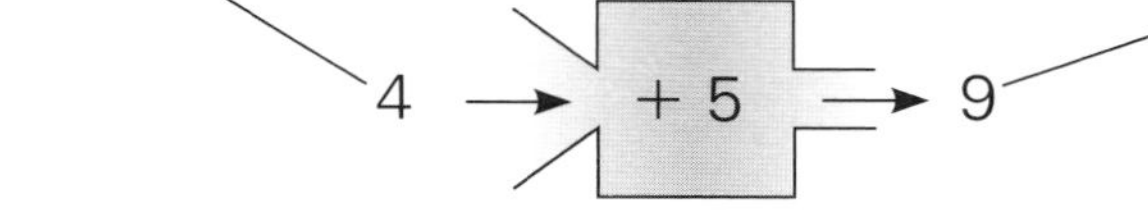

4   + 5   =   9

Complete these machines with the correct output.

a 5 → + 5 → ______

b

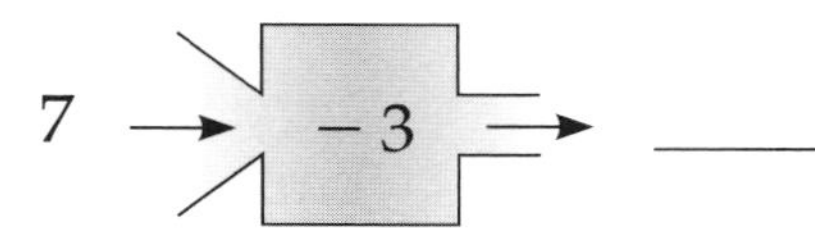

______

c 5 → × 3 → ______

d

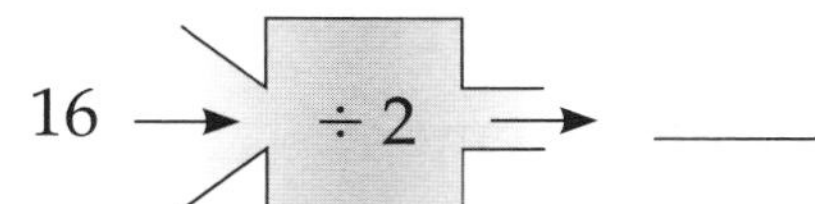

______

e 3 → + 9 → ______

f 12 → − 5 → ______

g 8 → × 3 → ______

h 14 → ÷ 7 → ______

2f Mapping

The relationship between the

before and **after** numbers is add 2:

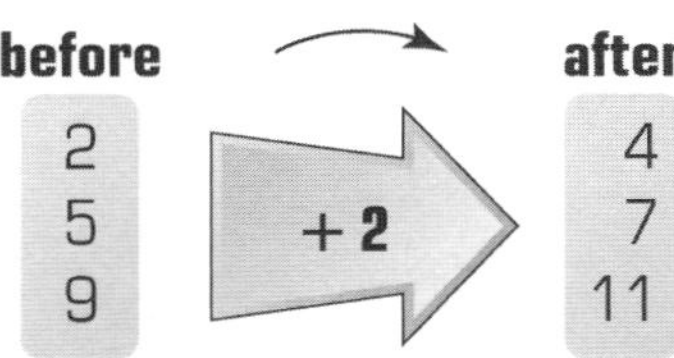

1 Write the relationship between the **before** and **after** numbers.

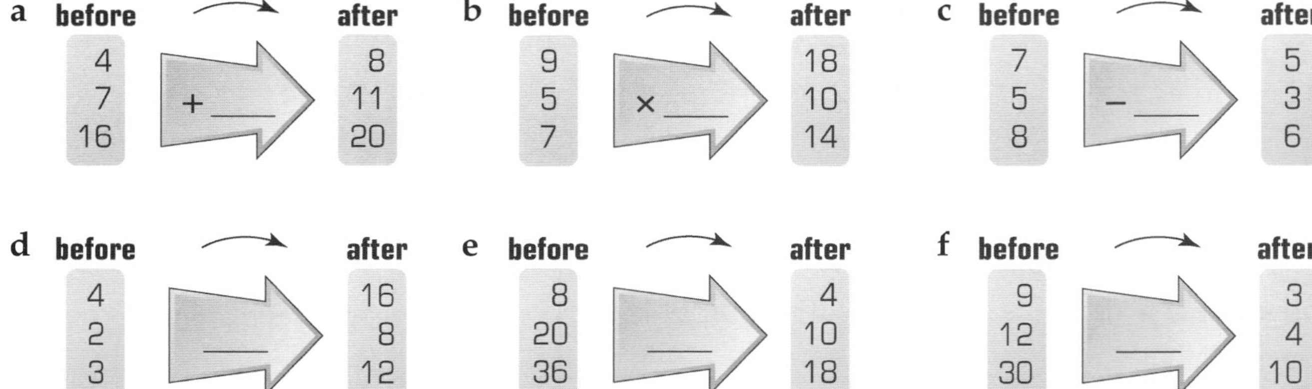

2 This drawing shows an ant and its enlargement in a microscope.

a Measure the lengths of the two images.

original length = _____ cm

enlarged length = _____ cm

b What is the relationship that describes the enlargement?

Answer: __________.

3a Measuring lines

I can do this page!

1 Write these units of measurement in the correct list.

month	kilogram	second	centimetre	
year	minute	tonne	week	kilometre
hour	gram	millimetre	day	metre

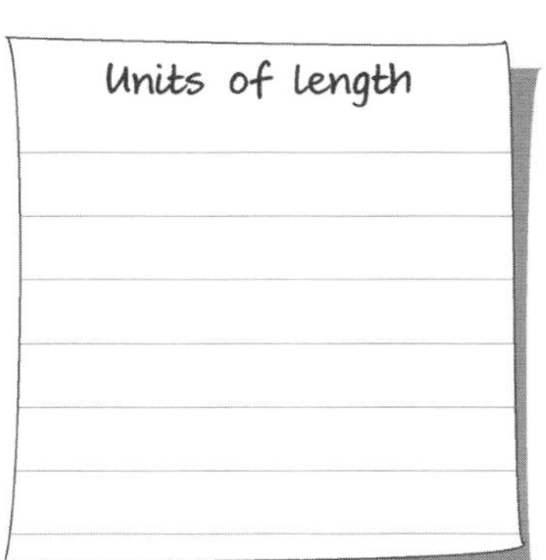

2 Measure these lines using a ruler.

a ______ cm

b ______ cm

c ______ cm

d ______ cm

e ______ cm

3 Measure the length and width of this rectangle and write on your answers.

3b Reading scales

1 Draw lines of these lengths on the rulers.

a 3.4 cm

b 6.7 cm

c 9.1 cm

2 What reading does each scale show?

Write your answer as a decimal.

A = ______

B = ______

C = ______

D = ______

E = ______

F = ______

G = ______

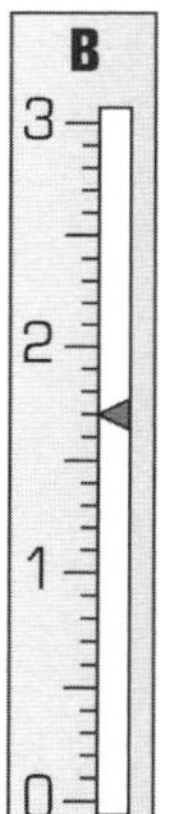

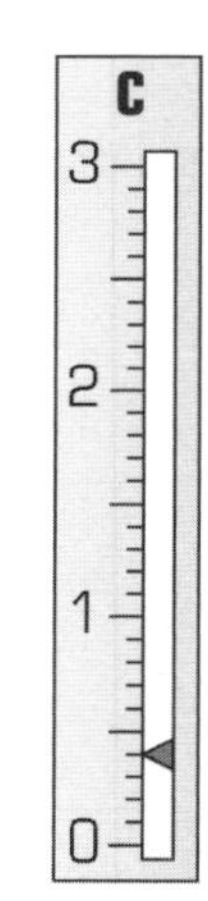

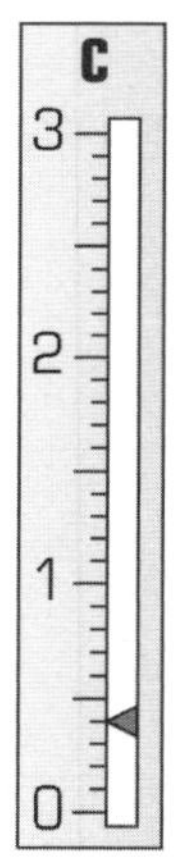

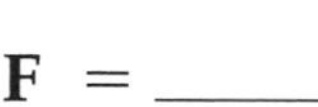

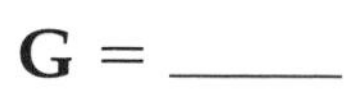

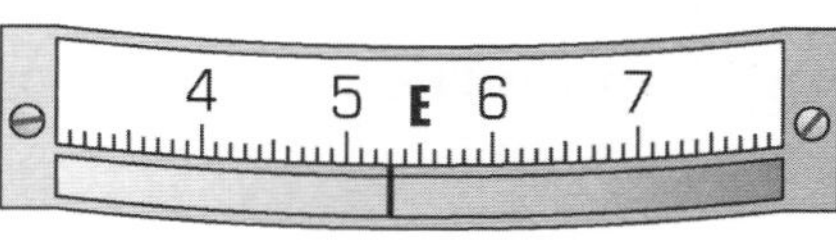

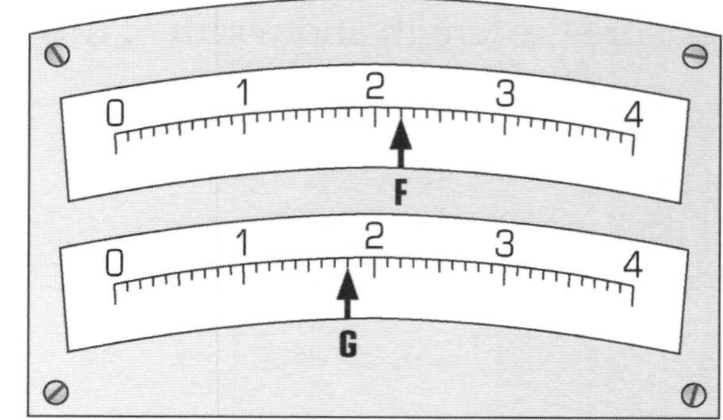

3c Time

I can do this page!

1 Put hands on each clock to show the time.

9 o'clock | half past one | 7:15 | quarter to five | five past six

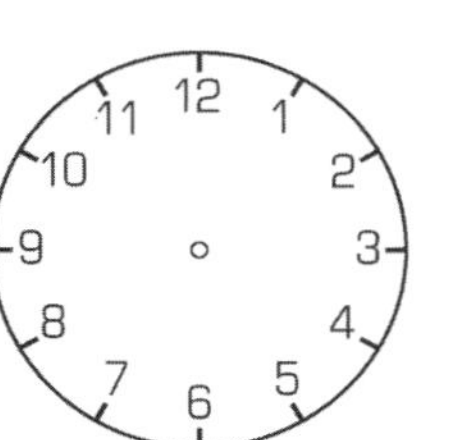
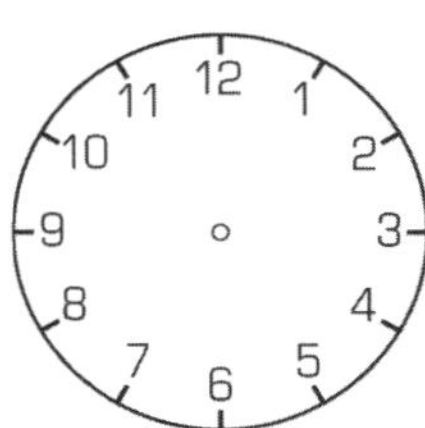
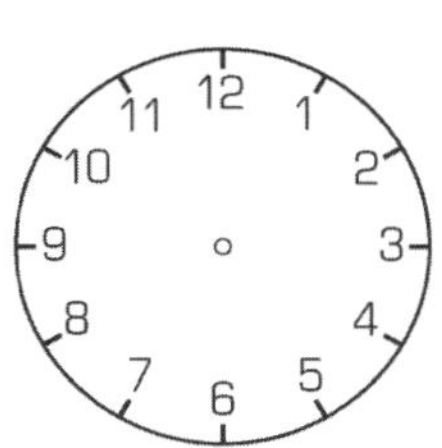
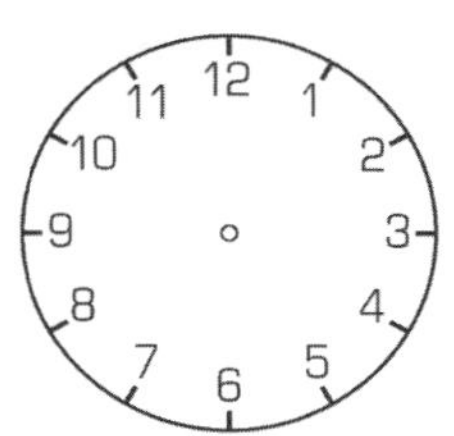
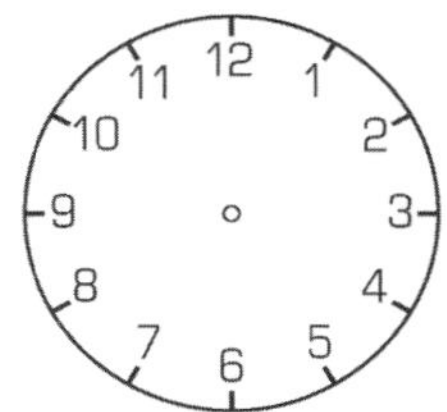

2 What times are shown on these clocks?

______ ______ ______ ______ ______

3 What times are shown on these clocks? Use **a.m.** for times before midday and **p.m.** for times after midday.

______ ______ ______

______ ______

Perimeter

I can do this page!

1 What is the perimeter of each shape?

a

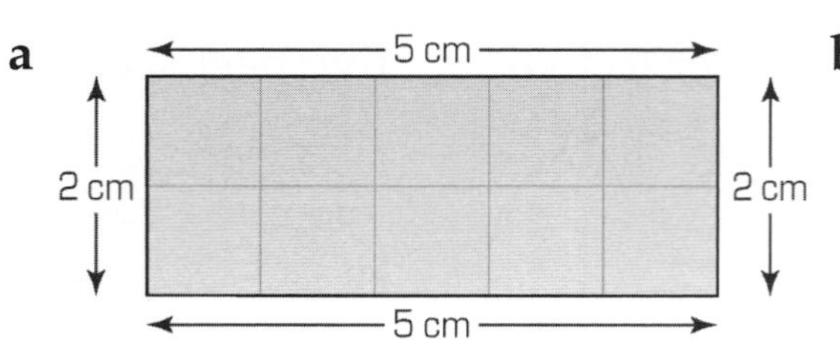

Perimeter = _____ cm

b

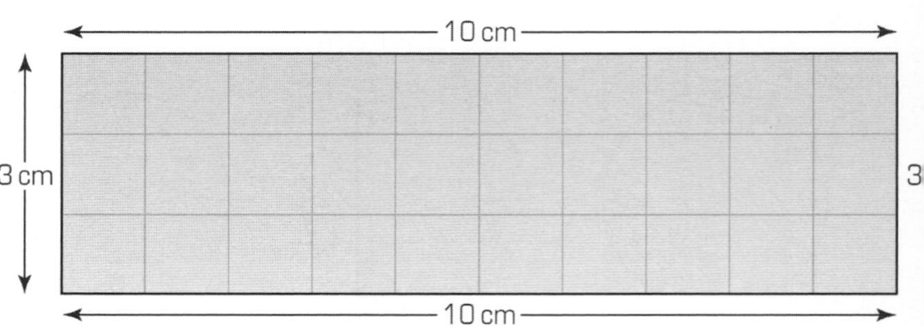

Perimeter = _____ cm

c

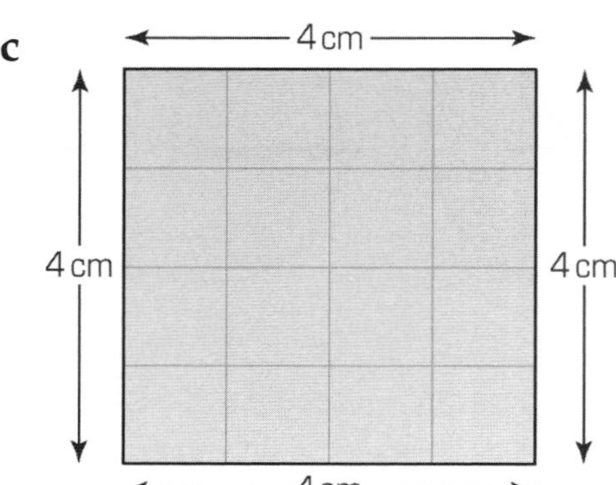

Perimeter = _____ cm

d

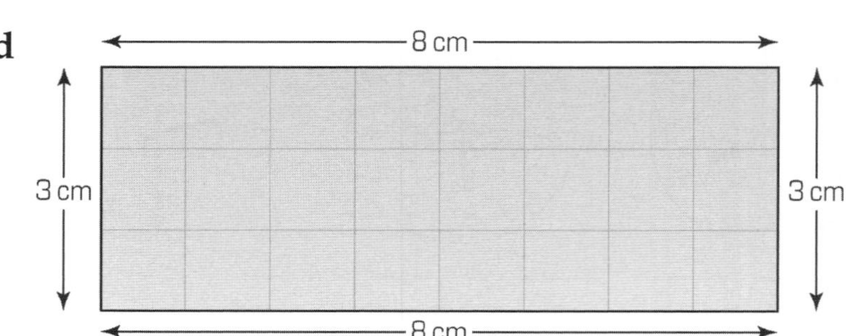

Perimeter = _____ cm

2 Measure the perimeter of each shape with a ruler.

a

Perimeter = _______ cm

b

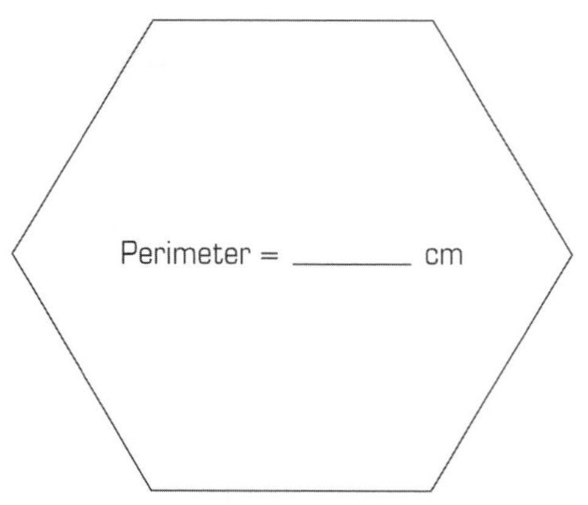

c

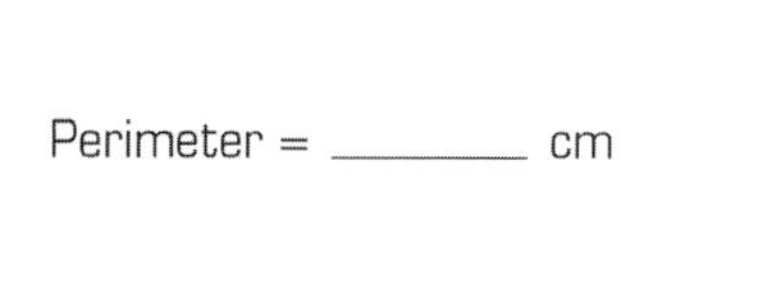

d

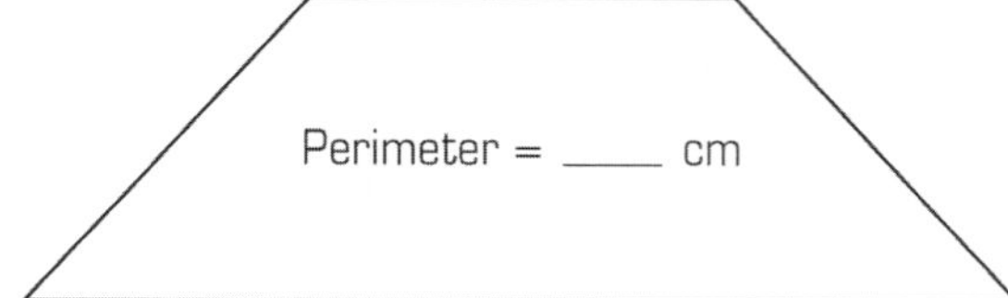

Area

This is a plan of the ground floor of a palace.

The measurements of each room are in metres.

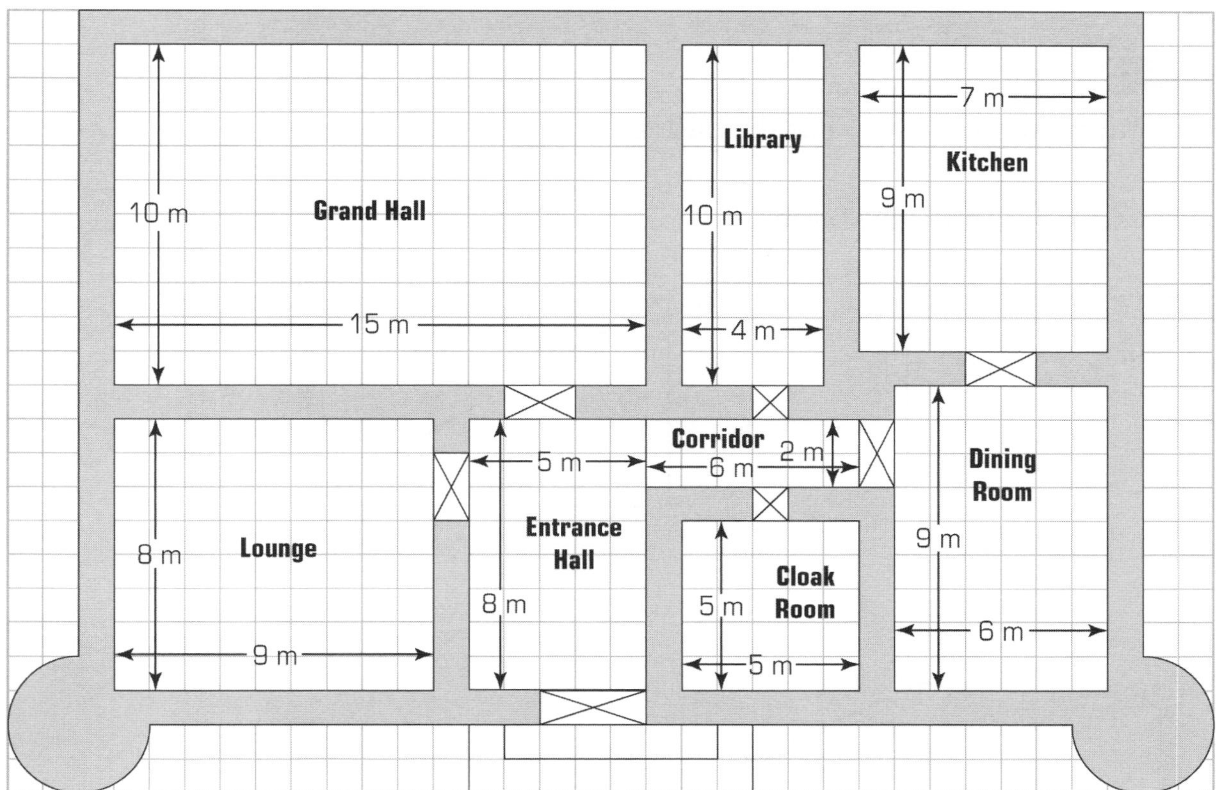

1 What is the perimeter of each room? Count the squares.

a The Cloak Room ____ m **b** The Library ____ m

c The Lounge ____ m **d** The Kitchen ____ m

e The Dining Room ____ m **f** The Grand Hall ____ m

2 What is the area of each room? Count the squares.

a The Cloak Room ____ m^2 **b** The Library ____ m^2

c The Lounge ____ m^2 **d** The Kitchen ____ m^2

e The Dining Room ____ m^2 **f** The Grand Hall ____ m^2

g The Entrance Hall ____ m^2 **h** The Corridor ____ m^2

3g Angles

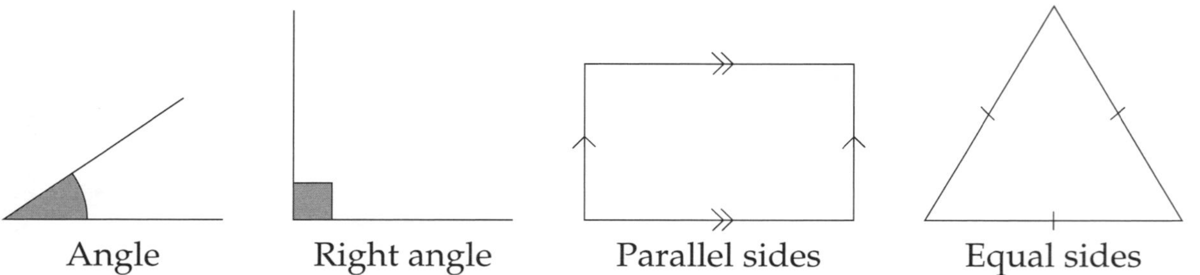

1 Mark the angles and sides in these shapes.

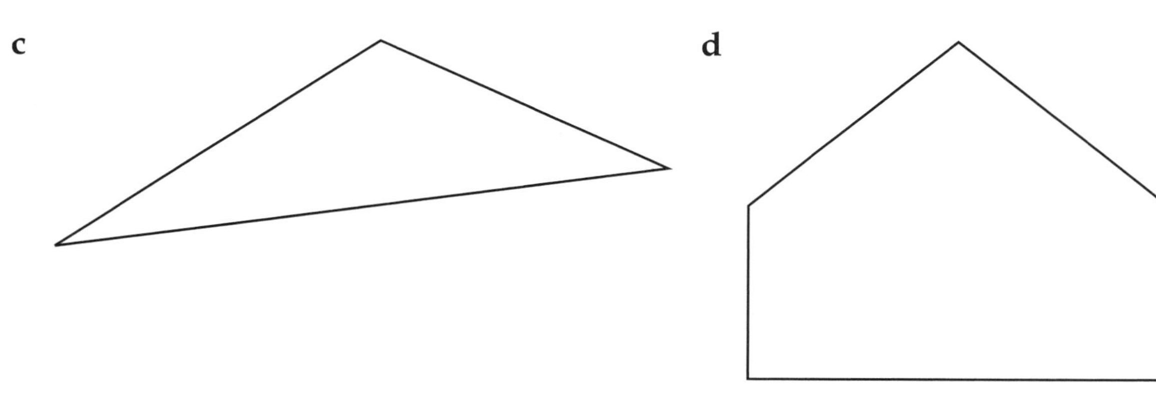

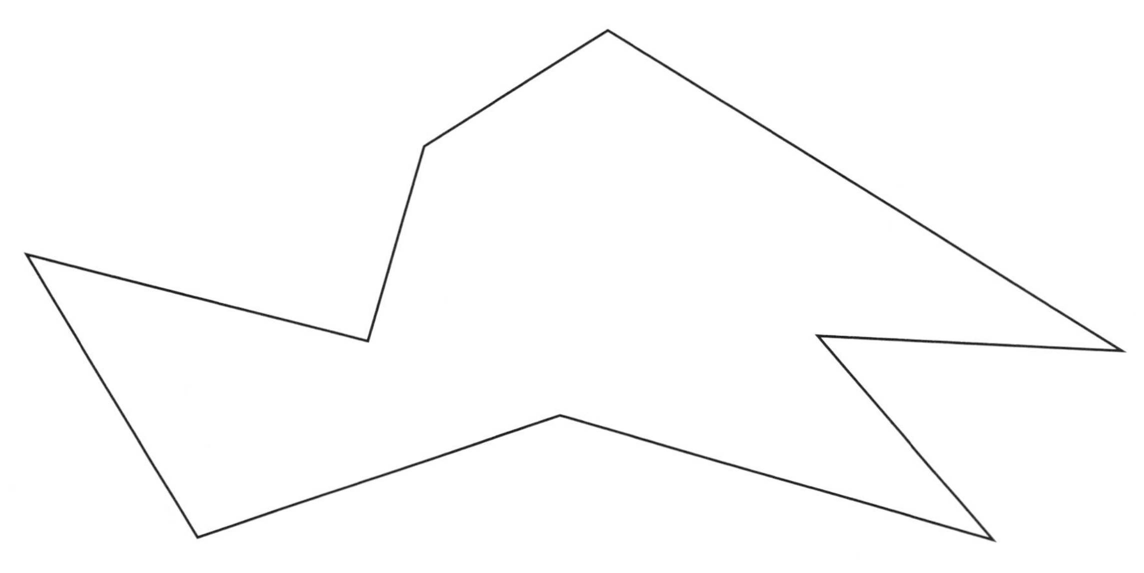

Maths life

Meet your match!

Use the information about sheep to answer the questions.

SHEEP

Sheep need to be in a herd, so you need more than one.

You can have three sheep per square kilometre.

Shear your sheep once a year.

One sheep can yield 5 kg of wool.

1 If my farm is 1 square kilometre, I can have ____ sheep.
My ____ sheep could yield ____ kg of wool.

2 If my farm is 2 square kilometres, I can have ____ sheep.
My ____ sheep could yield ____ kg of wool.

3 If my farm is 3 square kilometres, I can have ____ sheep.
My ____ sheep could yield ____ kg of wool.

Would it be better to shear your sheep in autumn or spring?

4a Fractions

1 Complete these sentences by looking at each shape. The first one is done for you.

a

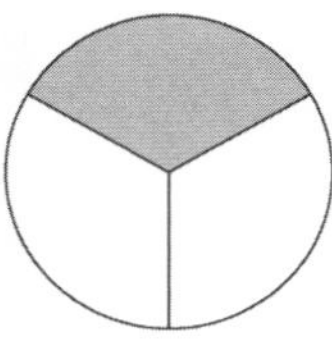

There are **3** parts.

1 part is shaded.

$\frac{1}{3}$ is shaded.

b

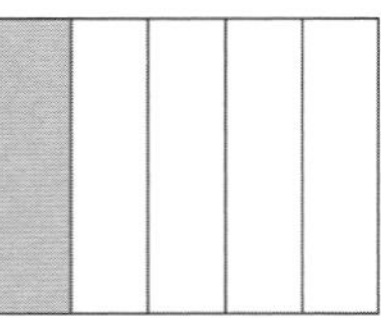

There are _____ parts.

_____ part is shaded.

_____ is shaded.

c

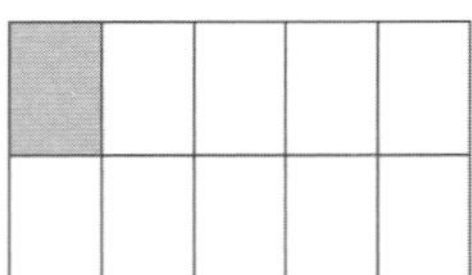

There are _____ parts.

_____ part is shaded.

_____ is shaded.

d

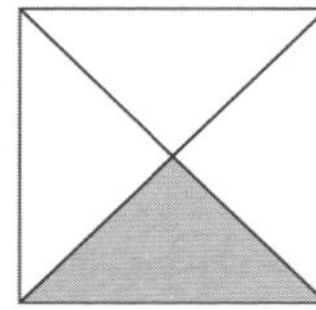

There are _____ parts.

_____ part is shaded.

_____ is shaded.

e

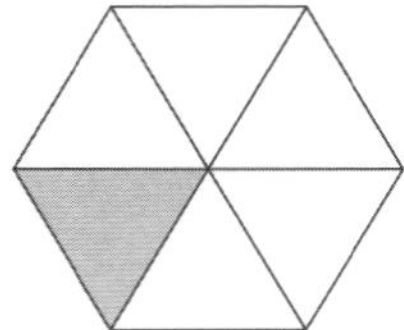

There are _____ parts.

_____ part is shaded.

_____ is shaded.

f

There are _____ parts.

_____ part is shaded.

_____ is shaded.

2

This shape is divided into 3 parts.

2 parts are shaded.

$\frac{2}{3}$ of the whole shape is shaded.

What fraction of each shape is shaded?

a

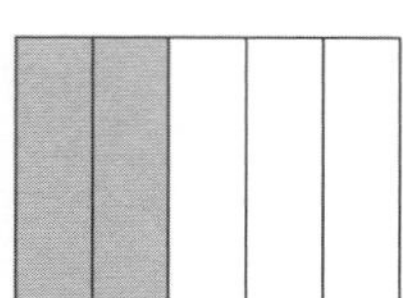

_____

b

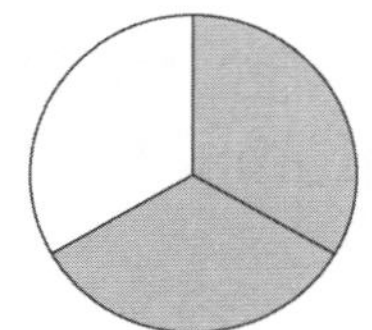

_____

c

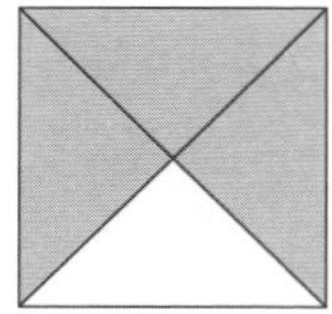

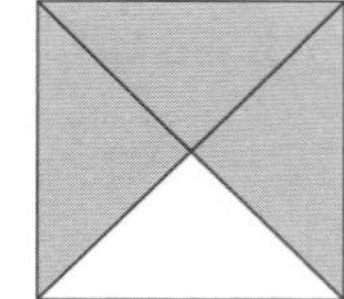

_____

d

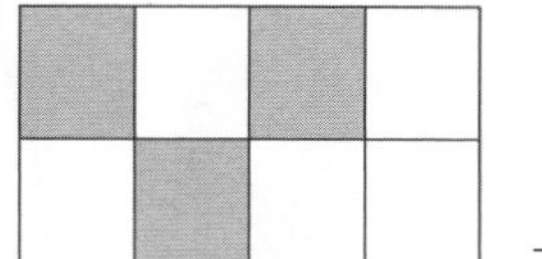

_____

e

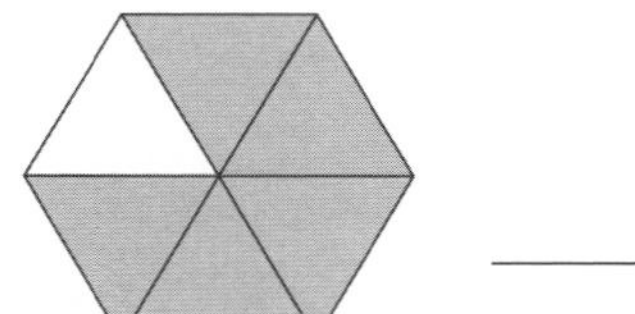

_____

f

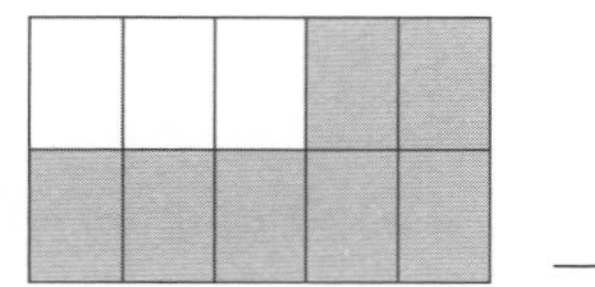

_____

4b Equivalent fractions

I can do this page!

1 Shade $\frac{1}{2}$ of each shape.

Write the fraction that is equivalent to $\frac{1}{2}$ in each drawing.

a

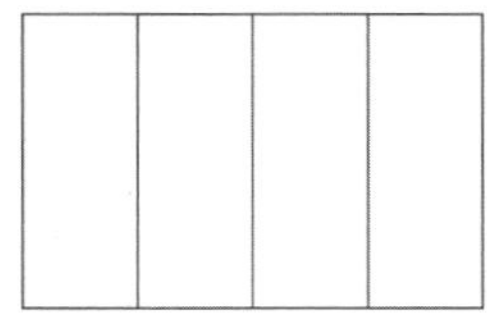

$\frac{1}{2}$ is the same as ☐

b

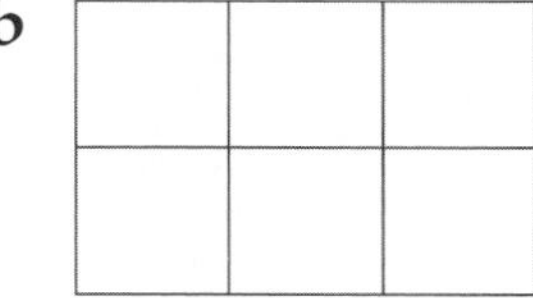

$\frac{1}{2}$ is the same as ☐

c

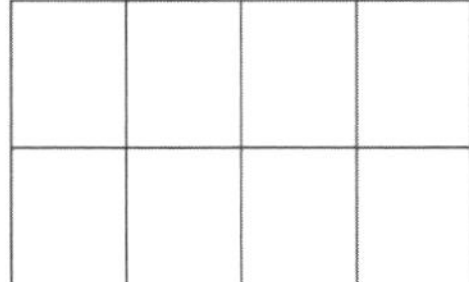

$\frac{1}{2}$ is the same as ☐

d

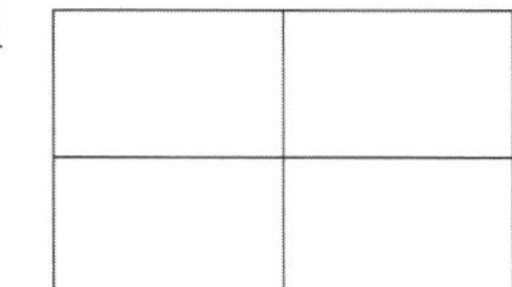

$\frac{1}{2}$ is the same as ☐

2 Shade $\frac{1}{5}$ of this shape.

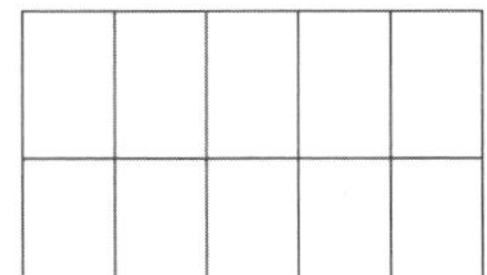

$\frac{1}{5}$ is the same as ☐

3 Shade $\frac{1}{4}$ of this shape.

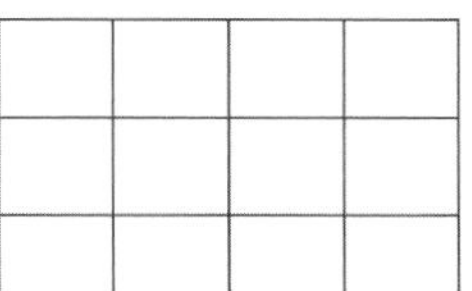

$\frac{1}{4}$ is the same as ☐

4 Shade $\frac{1}{6}$ of this shape.

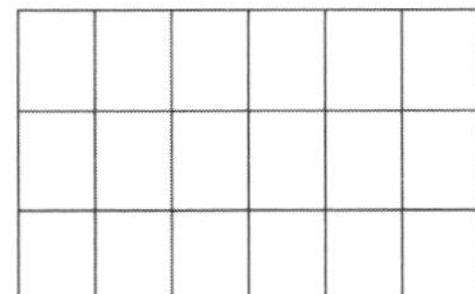

$\frac{1}{6}$ is the same as ☐

5 Shade $\frac{1}{5}$ of this shape.

$\frac{1}{5}$ is the same as ☐

4e Adding decimals

1 Write each amount as a decimal.

£0.10	£0.20					

2 Draw these amounts in the boxes.

a £1.25

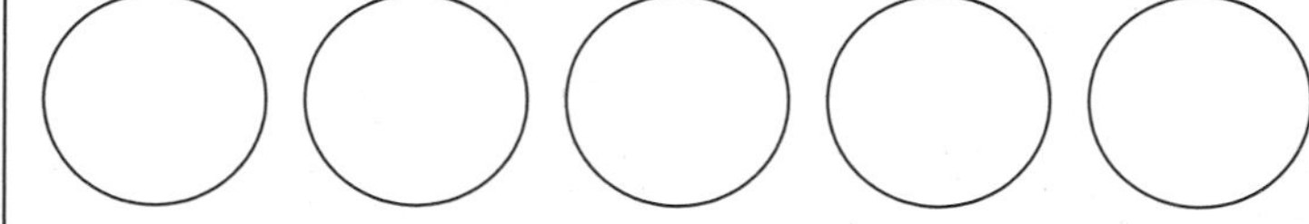

b £1.52

c £1.34

3 Add these decimals.

a £0.10 + £0.50 = ______

b £0.10 + £0.80 = ______

c £0.10 + £0.30 = ______

d £0.10 + £0.40 = ______

e £0.10 + £0.70 = ______

f £0.10 + £0.20 = ______

g £0.20 + £0.40 = ______

h £0.10 + £0.70 = ______

i £0.50 + £0.20 = ______

j £0.30 + £0.50 = ______

k £0.40 + £0.20 = ______

l £0.70 + £0.20 = ______

4f Fractions and decimals

1 How much of each shape is shaded?

Give your answer as a fraction and a decimal. The first is done for you.

a 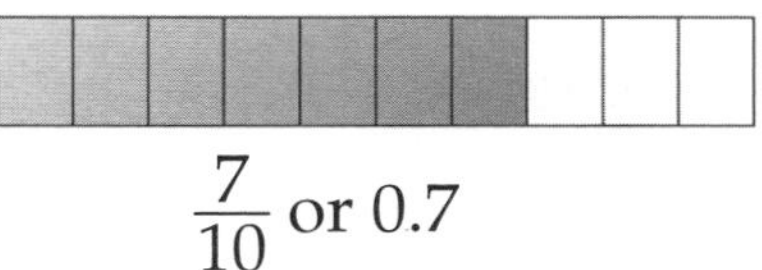

$\frac{7}{10}$ or 0.7

b 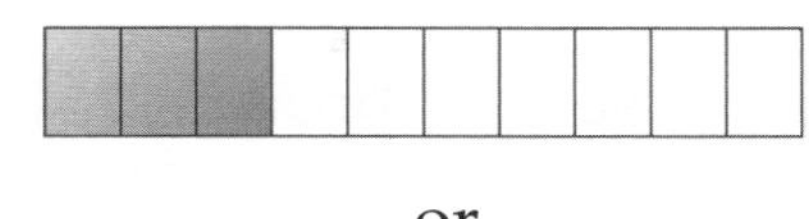

_____ or _____

c 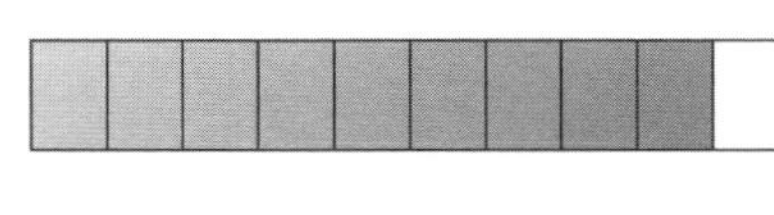

_____ or _____

d 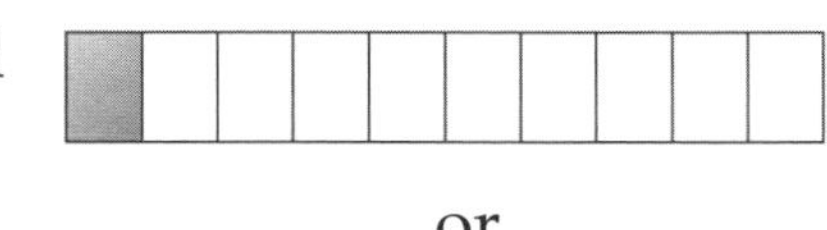

_____ or _____

e 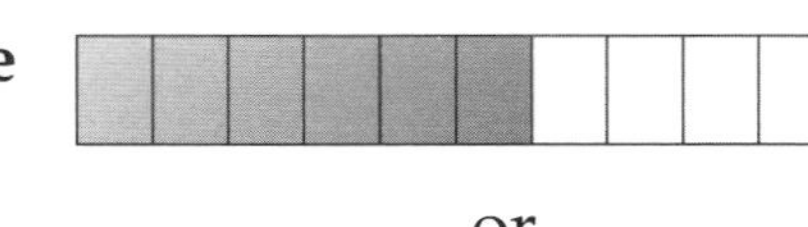

_____ or _____

f 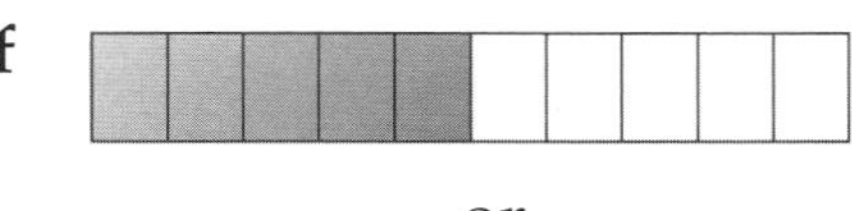

_____ or _____

2 Shade in these parts of this 10 × 10 square.

The first has been done for you.

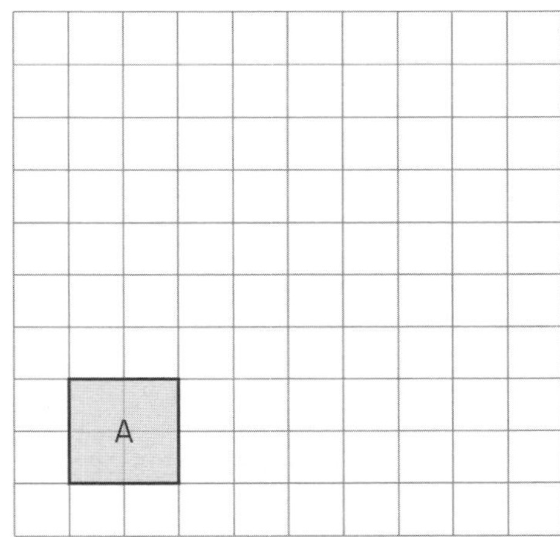

A $\frac{4}{100}$ or 0.04 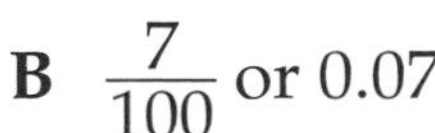 **B** $\frac{7}{100}$ or 0.07

C $\frac{5}{100}$ or 0.05 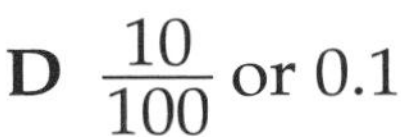 **D** $\frac{10}{100}$ or 0.1

E $\frac{14}{100}$ or 0.14 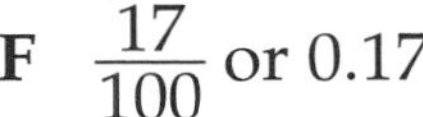 **F** $\frac{17}{100}$ or 0.17

3 Write these fractions as decimals.

The first one is done for you.

a $\frac{6}{100} = 0.06$ **b** $\frac{10}{100} =$ _____ **c** $\frac{16}{100} =$ _____

d $\frac{25}{100} =$ _____ **e** $\frac{65}{100} =$ _____ **f** $\frac{40}{100} =$ _____

4 Write these decimals as fractions.

The first one is done for you.

a $0.02 = \frac{2}{100}$ **b** 0.15 = _____ **c** 0.35 = _____

d 0.80 = _____ **e** 0.33 = _____ **f** 0.90 = _____

5a Data in lists and tables

1 Sort these 20 words onto the four lists.

hammer	France	Emily	blue	Ann	Canada	
hack-saw	green	brown	James	China	yellow	John
drill	Egypt	purple	Alfie	spade	Pakistan	pliers

Colours	Names	Tools	Countries
______	______	______	______
______	______	______	______
______	______	______	______
______	______	______	______
______	______	______	______

2 This is Joseph's receipt from the Supermarket.

a How many tins did Joseph buy? ______

b How much did he spend on vegetables? ______

c How much did he spend on meat? ______

d How much did he spend on tins? ______

e On which kind of product did he spend the **least**? ______

Super Supermarket	
Vegetables	£1.25
Vegetables	£0.50
Vegetables	£0.75
Meat	£3.50
Meat	£2.50
Tins	£1.20
Tins	£1.20
Tins	£1.20
Total	£___

5b Reading and drawing pictograms

Class 7P call out their favourite colours for a survey.

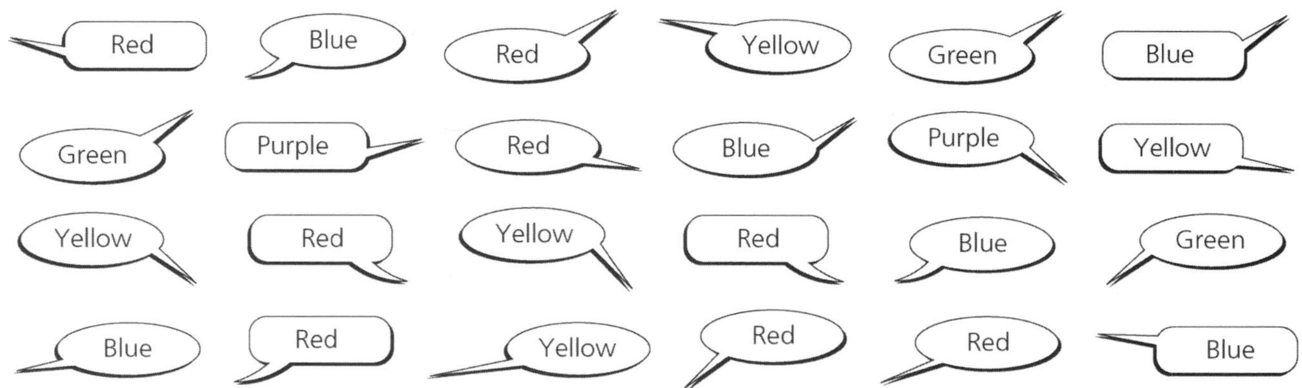

1 Count how many people called out each colour and write the numbers in the table. The first one has been done for you.

Colour	Number of people
Blue	6
Green	
Purple	
Red	
Yellow	

2 Complete this pictogram to show this data. Use ☺ to represent one person.

Favourite colour

Blue	
Green	
Purple	
Red	
Yellow	
	Number of students

Key: ☺ = ____________

3 How many students called out Blue?

____

4 What was the **most** popular colour?

____

5 What was the **least** popular colour?

____

Reading and drawing bar charts

1 Use the data to fill in this bar chart.

Fruit	Apple	Banana	Pear	Orange
Frequency	4	8	2	6

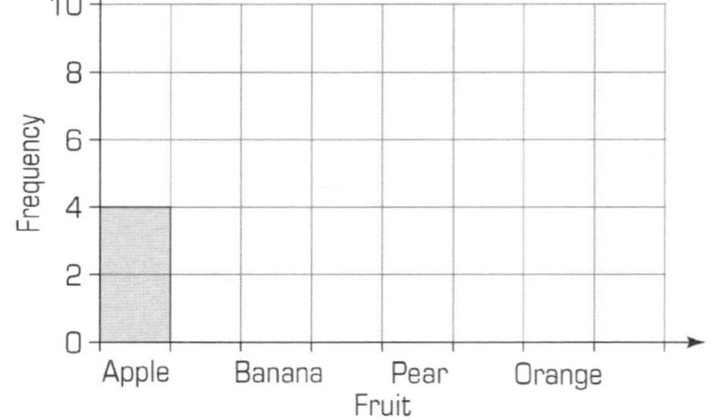

2 Use the data to complete this bar chart.

Number of pets	0	1	2	3	4
Frequency	14	10	4	6	2

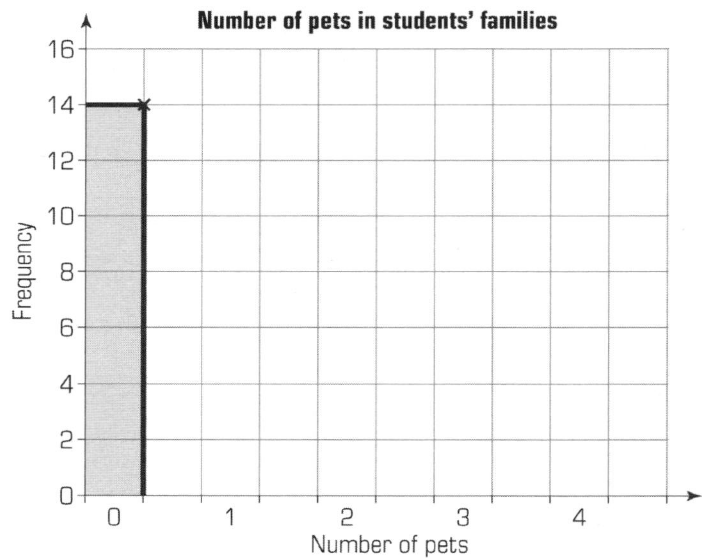

3 Use the data to draw a bar chart.

Bird	Number in garden
Jay	5
Robin	5
Magpie	10
Crow	20
Sparrow	15

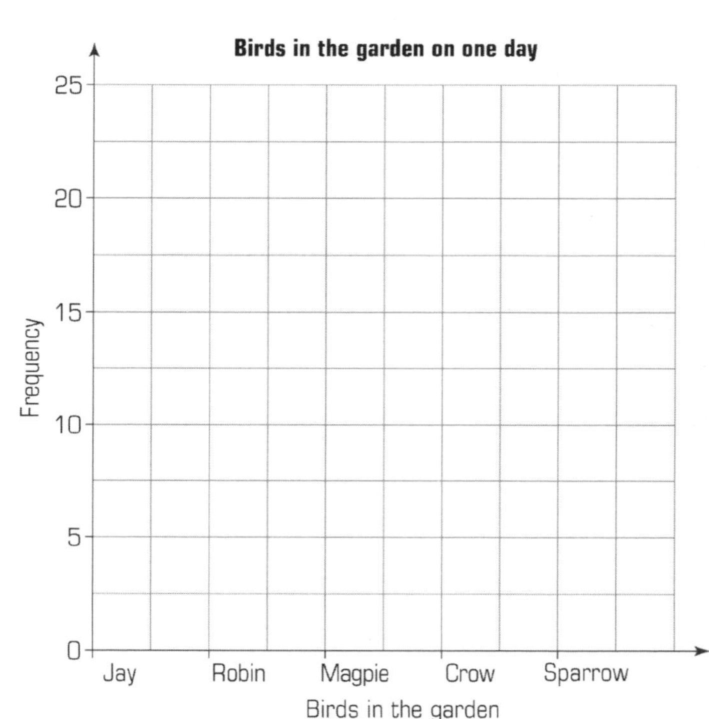

5f Reading diagrams

I can do this page!

1 This bar chart shows the sale of cars during one week.

The cars are sorted by colour.

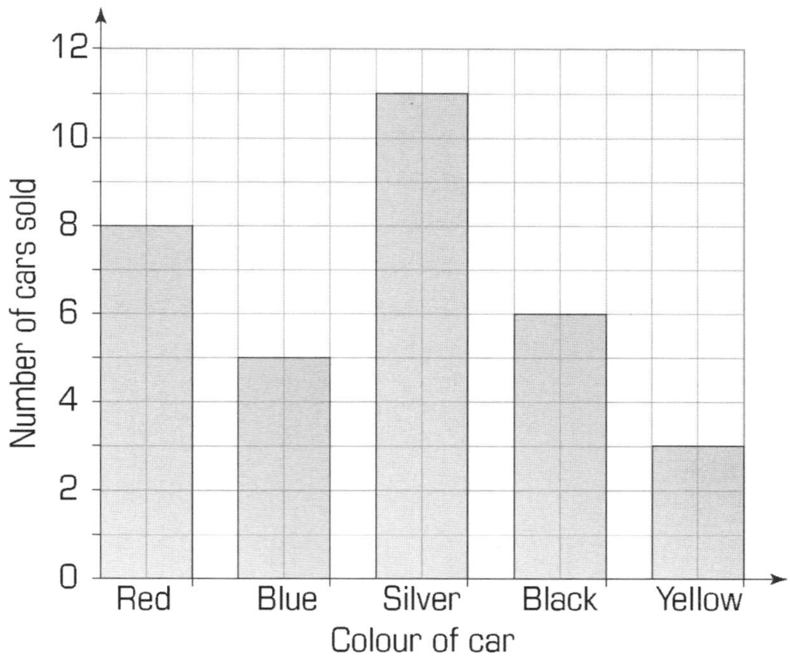

a Which colour was the biggest seller? ______________

b Which colour was the least popular? ______________

c 5 cars of one colour were sold. What colour were they? ______________

d How many cars were sold in total? ______________

2 Draw the data from the bar chart onto this pictogram.

Use the key to help you.

	Number of cars sold
Red	
Blue	
Silver	
Black	
Yellow	

Key:
= 2 cars
= 1 car

6a Operations

1 Put the correct operation in each calculation.

a 7 ☐ 8 = 15   **b** 6 ☐ 6 = 12   **c** 15 ☐ 10 = 5

d 15 ☐ 9 = 6   **e** 15 ☐ 6 = 9   **f** 10 ☐ 7 = 17

g 4 ☐ 5 = 20   **h** 4 ☐ 8 = 32   **i** 3 ☐ 4 = 12

j 9 ☐ 1 = 9   **k** 15 ☐ 5 = 3   **l** 50 ☐ 10 = 5

2 Put the correct operations in each calculation.

a 5 [+] 6 ☐ 3 = 8   **b** 7 [+] 3 ☐ 6 = 16

c 1 [+] 9 ☐ 4 = 14   **d** 10 [–] 5 ☐ 3 = 8

e 8 [+] 7 ☐ 3 = 18   **f** 11 [–] 3 ☐ 4 = 4

3 Fill in the missing numbers in each calculation.

a 3 + ☐ = 7   **b** ☐ ÷ 3 = 7

c 6 × ☐ = 30   **d** 45 – 10 = ☐

e 10 × 8 = ☐   **f** 36 ÷ 4 = ☐

g 13 – ☐ = 6   **h** 35 + 25 = ☐

Using symbols

1 Josh keeps some of his marbles in a bag.

Can you tell exactly how many marbles are in Josh's bag, without guessing?

Circle the correct answer: Yes or No

2 Josh uses t to stand for the number of marbles in his bag.

He has t marbles in the bag and another 4 marbles.

t 4

a How many marbles does Josh have altogether?

Circle the correct answer.

$t - 4$ marbles $t + 4$ marbles $4 - t$ marbles

b Josh won 6 more marbles.

How many marbles does he now have altogether?

Circle the correct answer.

$t + 4$ marbles 10 marbles $t + 10$ marbles 2 marbles

3 **a** These parcels weigh n kilograms altogether.

The small parcel to the side weighs 8 kilograms.

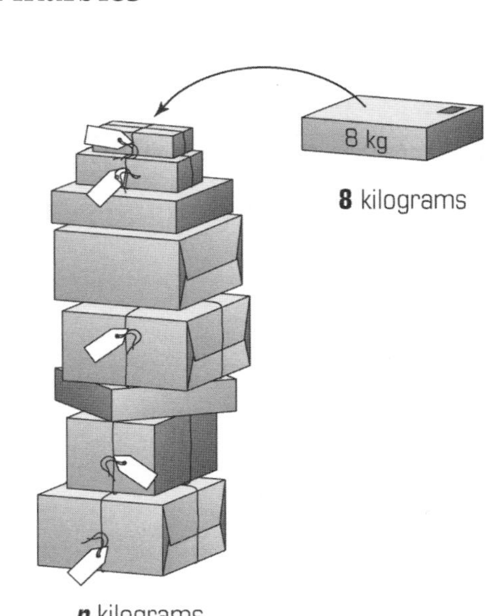

Add the small parcel to the big pile.

What is the total weight in kg?

Circle the correct answer.

$n + 8$ $n - 8$ $8 - n$ $n \times 8$

b Add another parcel weighing 12 kilograms to the pile.

What is the new total weight in kg?

Circle the correct answer.

$n + 12$ 12 20 $n + 20$

6d Substitution

I can do this page!

Small boxes hold 3 doughnuts.

Medium boxes hold 6 doughnuts.

Large boxes hold 10 doughnuts.

You can use symbols to represent the numbers of doughnuts in each box:

$s = 3$ $m = 6$ $l = 10$

For a small box and two extra doughnuts:

$s + 2$ means $3 + 2$

so $s + 2 = 5$

1 Draw $s + 1$ doughnuts:

2 Draw $s - 2$ doughnuts:

3 Draw $m + 3$ doughnuts:

4 Draw $m - 1$ doughnuts:

5 Draw $m - 3$ doughnuts:

6 Draw $l - 3$ doughnuts:

7 Draw $s + s$ doughnuts:

8 Draw $s + m$ doughnuts:

7a Rounding

When rounding to the nearest 10

- if the last number is 5 or above you round up
- if the last number is less then 5 you round down.

71 72 73 74	75 76 77 78 79
These will round down to 70.	These will round up to 80.

1 Circle the numbers that would round down.

23 98 73 81 37 59 65 42 94 26 46 51

2 Circle the numbers that would round up.

53 78 26 55 94 24 18 83 16 82 49 37

3 Round these numbers down.

a 72 → ☐ **b** 51 → ☐ **c** 34 → ☐ **d** 21 → ☐

e 13 → ☐ **f** 82 → ☐ **g** 63 → ☐ **h** 44 → ☐

4 Round these numbers up.

a 79 → ☐ **b** 57 → ☐ **c** 36 → ☐ **d** 85 → ☐

e 68 → ☐ **f** 25 → ☐ **g** 17 → ☐ **h** 48 → ☐

5 Round these amounts to the nearest £ 10.

a £ 88 → ☐ **b** £ 51 → ☐ **c** £ 14 → ☐

d £ 75 → ☐ **e** £ 12 → ☐ **f** £ 47 → ☐

g £ 33 → ☐ **h** £ 76 → ☐ **i** £ 29 → ☐

j £ 64 → ☐ **k** £ 48 → ☐ **l** £ 22 → ☐

7b Mental methods of multiplication

When you multiply a number by 10 you move the digits one place to the left:

$3 \times 10 = 30$ $16 \times 10 = 160$

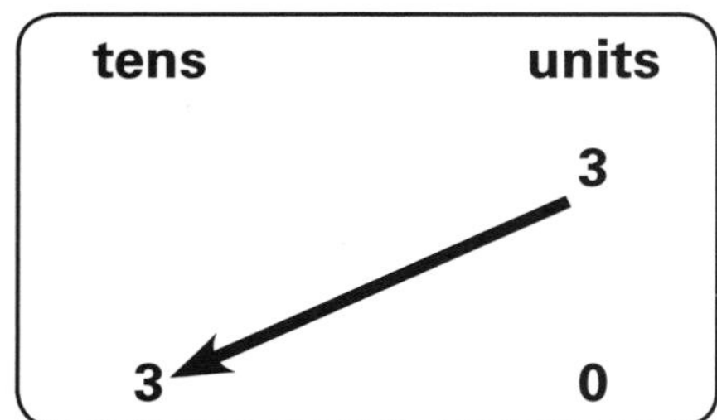

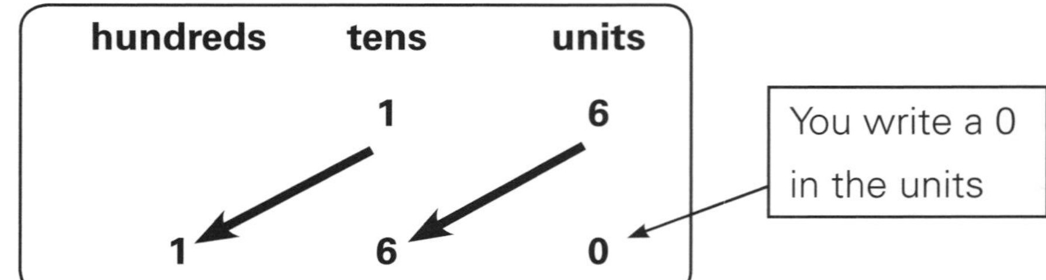

1 Multiply these numbers by 10. Put the digits in the correct place.

Remember to put a 0 in the empty units place.

		hundreds	tens	units
a	$6 \times 10 =$			
b	$9 \times 10 =$			
c	$5 \times 10 =$			
d	$8 \times 10 =$			
e	$10 \times 10 =$			

		hundreds	tens	units
f	$12 \times 10 =$			
g	$23 \times 10 =$			
h	$40 \times 10 =$			
i	$51 \times 10 =$			
j	$83 \times 10 =$			

2 Double each of the numbers in the 'arrow' boxes.

Write your answers in the circles.

× 2

70, 5, 50, 6, 60, 9, 90, 7

7c Written methods of multiplication

1 Complete these calculations.

a $2 \times 4 =$ _____ b $3 \times 6 =$ _____ c $5 \times 6 =$ _____

d $8 \times 7 =$ _____ e $5 \times 4 =$ _____ f $6 \times 8 =$ _____

g _____ $\times 4 = 16$ h $3 \times$ _____ $= 24$ i _____ $\times 4 = 36$

2 Split up these numbers into tens and units.

a 16 is the same as [10] + [ ] b 11 is the same as [10] + [ ]

c 19 is the same as [10] + [ ] d 13 is the same as [10] + [ ]

3 Fill in the boxes to multiply these numbers.

a 16×4

16 is [10] + [ ]

$10 \times 4 =$ [ ]

$6 \times 4 =$ [ ]

So $16 \times 4 =$ [40] + [ ]

= [ ]

b 19×3

19 is [ ] + [9]

$10 \times 3 =$ [ ]

$9 \times 3 =$ [ ]

So $19 \times 3 =$ [ ] + [ ]

= [ ]

c 15×7

15 is [10] + [ ]

$10 \times 7 =$ [ ]

$5 \times 7 =$ [ ]

So $15 \times 7 =$ [ ] + [ ]

= [ ]

d 14×4

14 is [ ] + [ ]

$10 \times 4 =$ [ ]

$4 \times 4 =$ [ ]

So $14 \times 4 =$ [ ] + [ ]

= [ ]

7d Division

When you divide a number by 10, you move the digits one place to the right.

hundreds	tens	units	
3	2	0	÷ 10
	3	2	

Divide these numbers by 10. Move the digits one place to the right.

The first one is done for you.

	calculation	hundreds	tens	units
1			9	0
	90 ÷ 10 =			9
2			3	0
	30 ÷ 10 =			
3				
	50 ÷ 10 =			
4				
	120 ÷ 10 =			
5				
	170 ÷ 10 =			
6				
	230 ÷ 10 =			
7				
	540 ÷ 10 =			
8				
	860 ÷ 10 =			
9				
	490 ÷ 10 =			
10				
	800 ÷ 10 =			

7e Division problems

Use each number line to work out the division.

The hints are there to help you.

1 $32 \div 4 =$ ☐

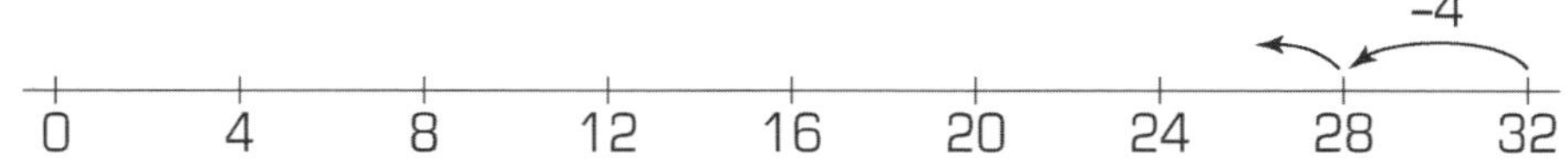

Jump backwards until you reach 0

2 $40 \div 5 =$ ☐

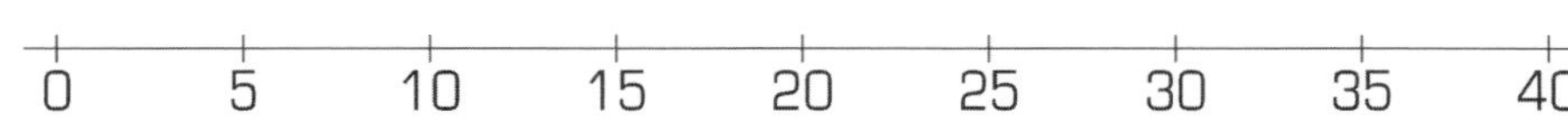

3 $27 \div 3 =$ ☐

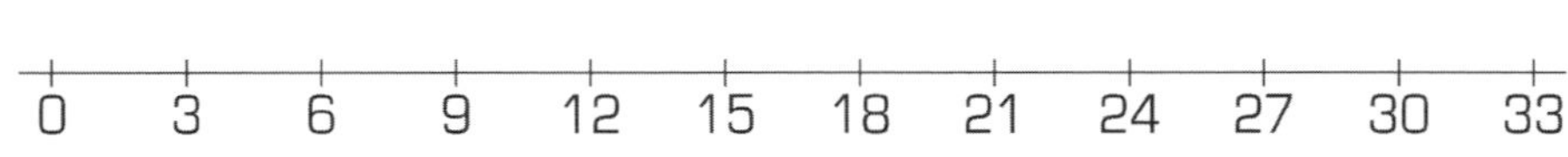

Be careful where you start.

4 $25 \div 5 =$ ☐

Write your own numbers on the line.

Count down in 5s.

5 $48 \div 4 =$ ☐

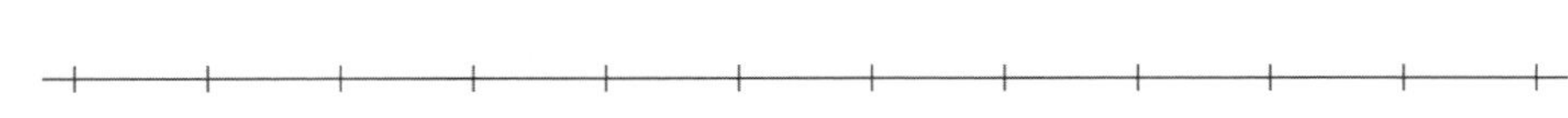

Write your own numbers on the line.

Start at 48 and count down in 4s.

7g Metric units

1 The soda can contains 70 ml.

The cola can contains 75 ml.

a Which can contains the most? ______________________

b How much more? ______________________

2 The butter weighs 200 g.

The margarine weighs 250 g.

a Which weighs more? ______________________

b How much more? ______________________

3 **a** Which roll of tape is the longest? ______________________

b Which roll of tape is the shortest? ______________________

c How much longer is B than C? ______________________

d How much longer is A than B? ______________________

e How much shorter is C than A? ______________________

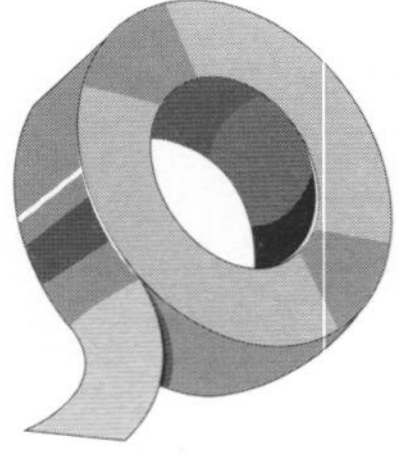

B = 20 m

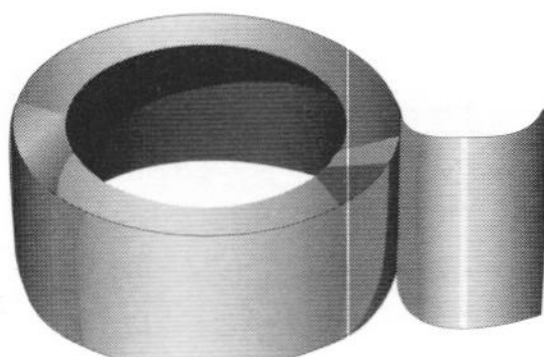

7h Measuring and accuracy

1 Estimate each of these measures.

Write the units that you are using to estimate each measure.

Item	Estimate	Units
Length of your classroom		(m) metres
Height of the classroom door		
Height of your friend		
Weight of your Maths book		
How many students in your school		students
Cost of a portion of fish and chips		
Weight of a cricket ball		
Flight time from London to New York	7	
The length of a marathon race		
The cost to run your school for one year		

2 The distance from London to Edinburgh is about 600 km.

Estimate the distance in km between these towns.

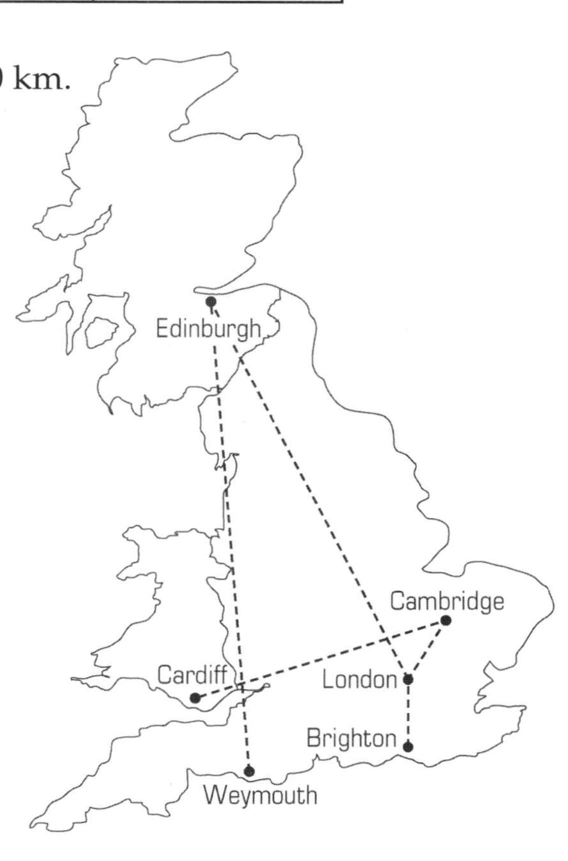

a London to Cambridge

b Brighton to London

c Cardiff to Cambridge

d Edinburgh to Weymouth

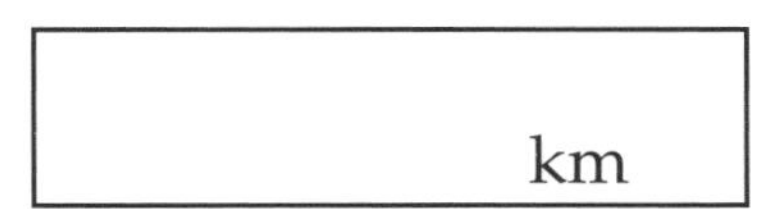

Introducing probability

1 Read the sentences and decide if the events are certain, uncertain or impossible.

Put the correct letter after the sentence.

C certain U uncertain I impossible

a	All cars will need new tyres.	
b	All cars will need new tyres tomorrow.	
c	Cars have number plates.	
d	Cars have 4 doors.	
e	All buses are red.	
f	Buses carry passengers.	
g	You sit on a bus.	
h	Trains travel along the road.	
i	Trains have 4 carriages.	
j	Planes fly in the air.	
k	Trains travel on rails.	
l	Roads have yellow lines.	
m	Cars travel at the speed limit.	
n	Boats are used for fishing.	
o	Children enjoy playing with toy cars.	
p	A space ship will land in the park.	

8d More probability

I can do this page!

When you spin two coins, there are three ways they can land.

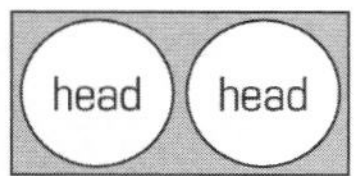

or

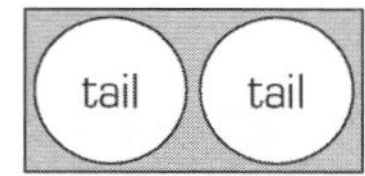

or

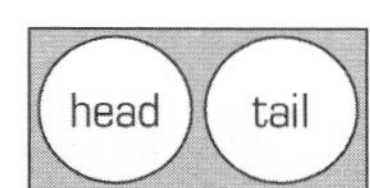

Follow these steps to see if you can guess which way will come up!

You will need two coins.

1. Guess a result – two heads, two tails or a head and a tail. You can write: HH, TT or HT.
2. Spin two coins.
3. If the guess is correct follow the tick (✓) to the next level. If not, follow the cross (✗).
4. Repeat until you reach the bottom level. This shows your percentage of correct guesses.

You can play the game with other students – take it in turns to guess and use a different colour to mark your results.

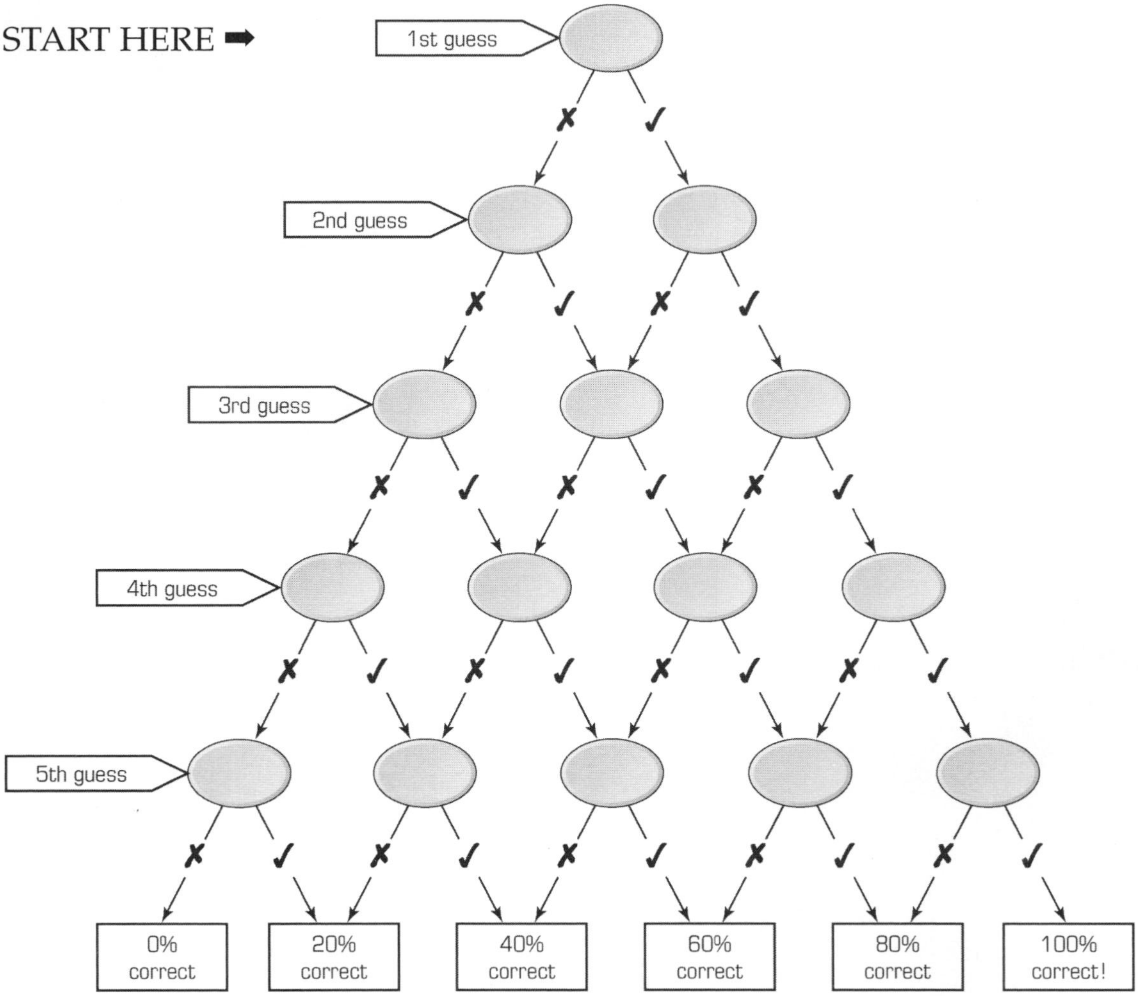

START HERE ➡

1st guess

2nd guess

3rd guess

4th guess

5th guess

0% correct	20% correct	40% correct	60% correct	80% correct	100% correct!

Maths life

Choosing the right route

I can do this page!

Valley Mountain Rescue wants to know how much money they could make if they sold these numbers of items.

Cakes £1

Tea 50p

1 a 50 cakes sold = £_____

b 100 cakes sold = £_____

c 50 teas sold = £_____

d 100 teas sold = £_____

e 50 cakes and 50 teas sold = £_____

f 200 cakes and 200 teas sold = £_____

g 200 cakes and 100 teas sold = £_____

Should they charge more money for a cake and a tea?

How much would you pay for a cake and a tea?

Cake Stall!

Saturday

15 April

1.30pm - 4.30pm

The Valley Community Centre

9b Angle measure

1 What is the size of each angle?

Give your answer in degrees (°).

a

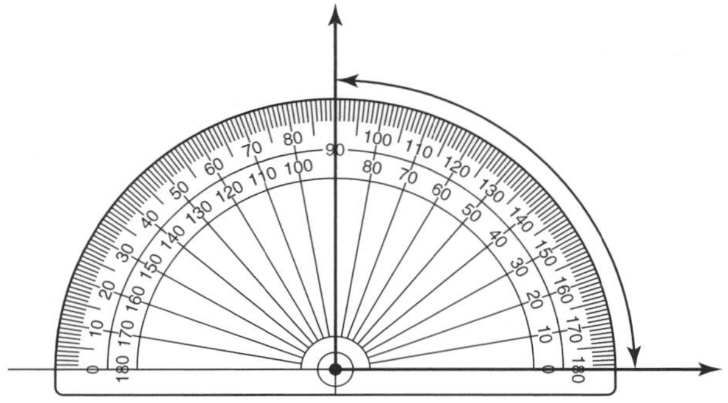

b

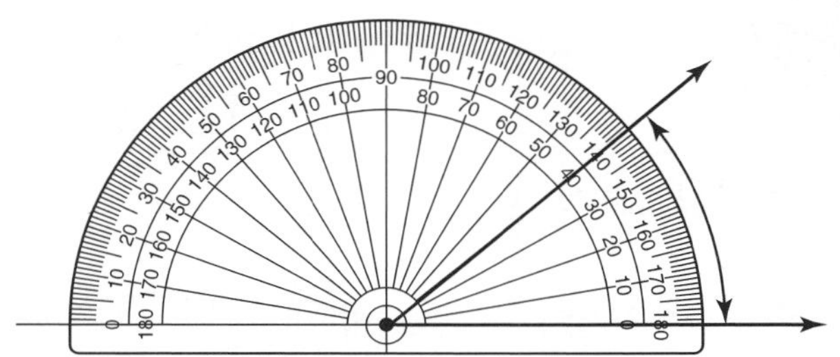

c

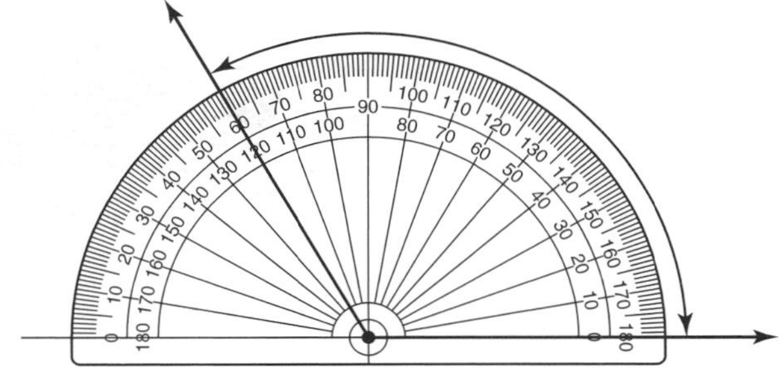

d

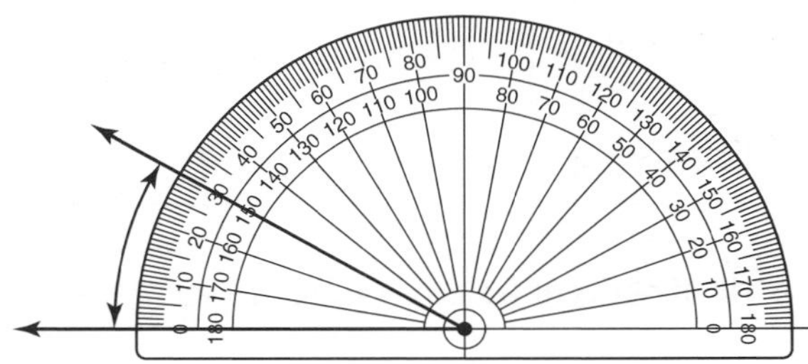

e

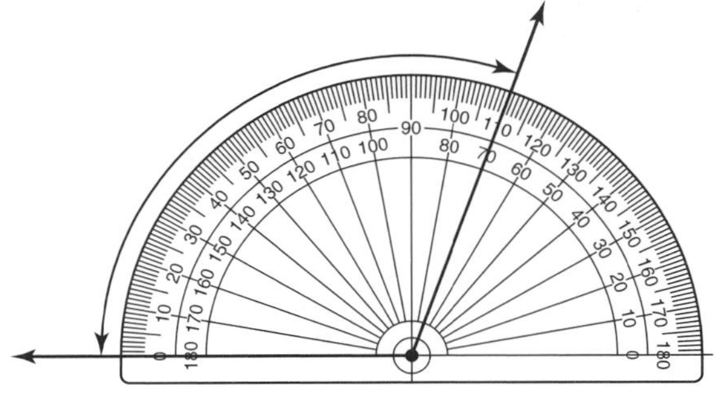

f

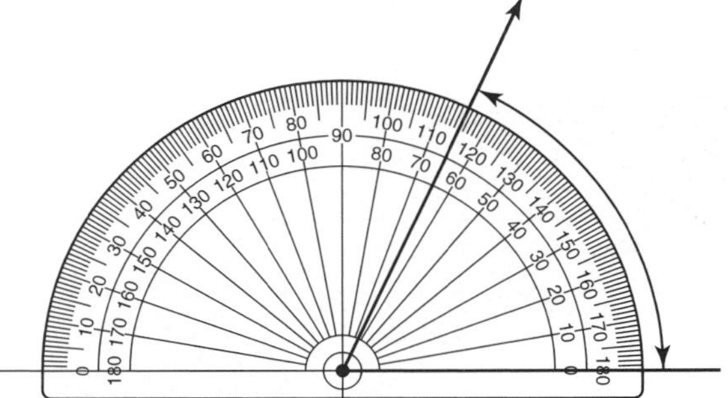

9b² Measuring and drawing angles

1 Draw these angles on this protractor.

a 100° **b** 40° **c** 140°

d 70° **e** 120°

Label each angle. The first has been done for you.

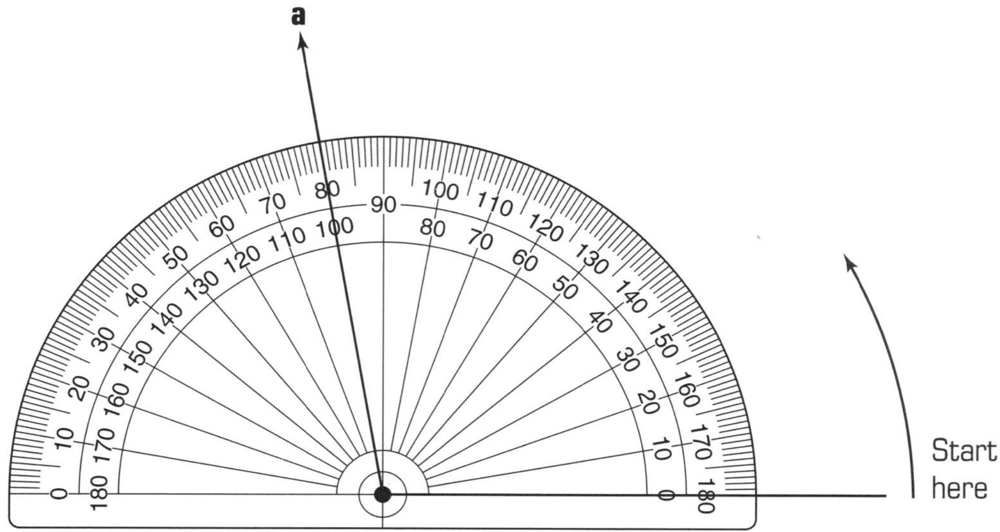

2 Use a protractor to draw these angles.

Place the cross on the dot.

a 50°

b 80°

c 130°

d 20°

9e 3-D shapes

Fill in the table for these shapes

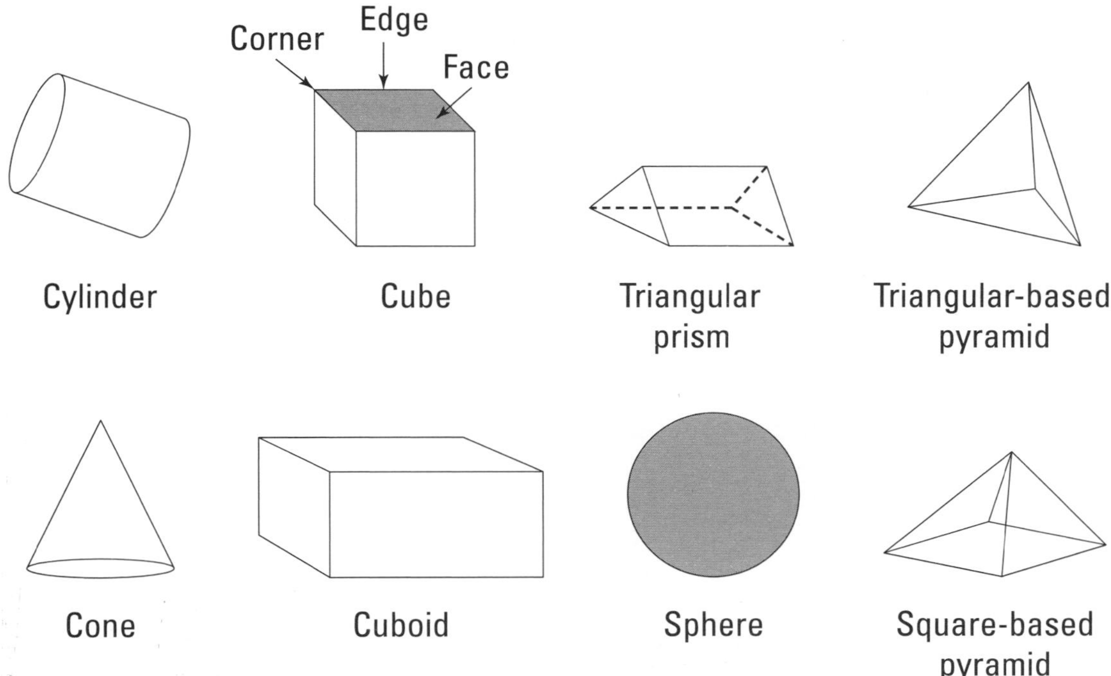

Shape	Faces	Edges	Corners
cylinder	3	2	0
cube			
cone			
cuboid			
triangular prism			
triangular-based pyramid			
square-based pyramid			
sphere			

10a Factors

I can do this page!

You can arrange these 10 counters into two rectangle patterns.

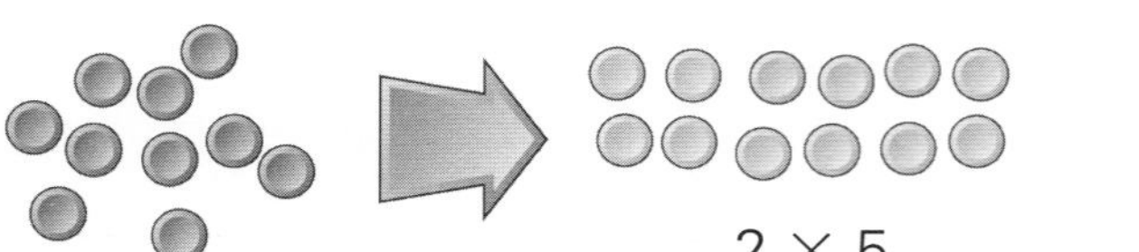

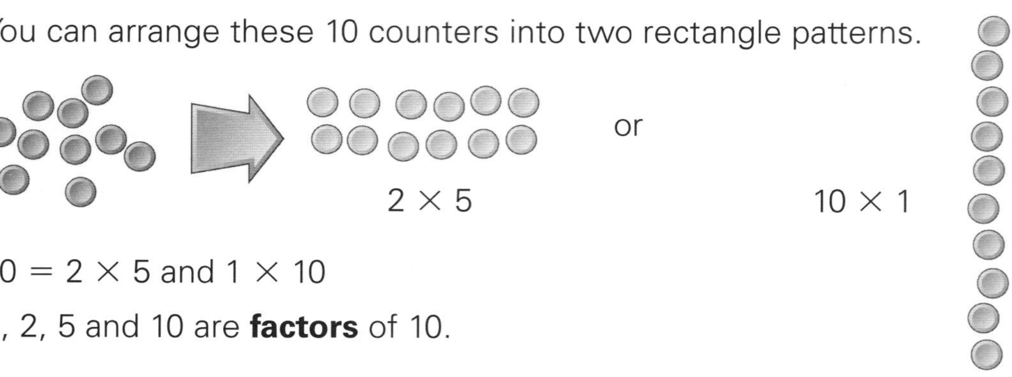

2×5 or 10×1

$10 = 2 \times 5$ and 1×10

1, 2, 5 and 10 are **factors** of 10.

1 a Arrange these 12 counters into 3 different rectangle patterns on this grid:

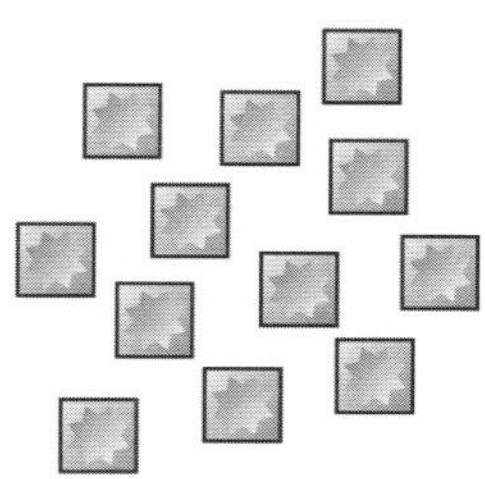

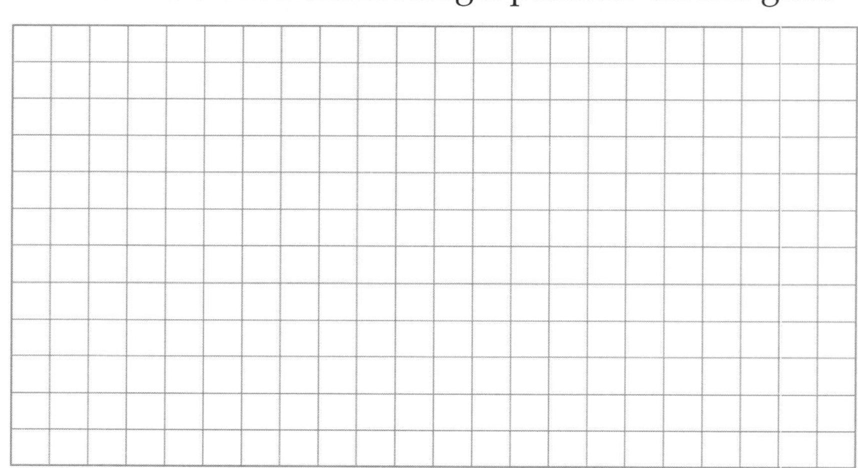

b List all the factors of 12: ______________________

2 a There are 18 counters here.

Draw rectangle patterns to list all the factors of 18.

There are 3 different rectangle patterns.

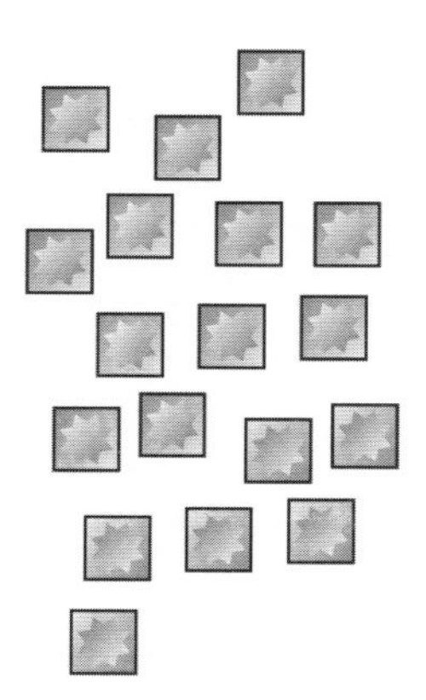

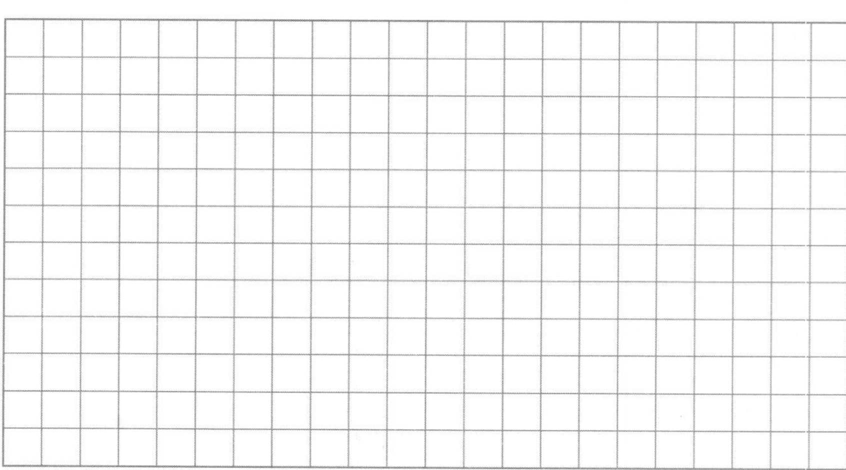

b List all the factors of 18: ______________________

Multiples

1 Multiply the numbers in the arrow boxes by 3.

Write your answers in the circles.

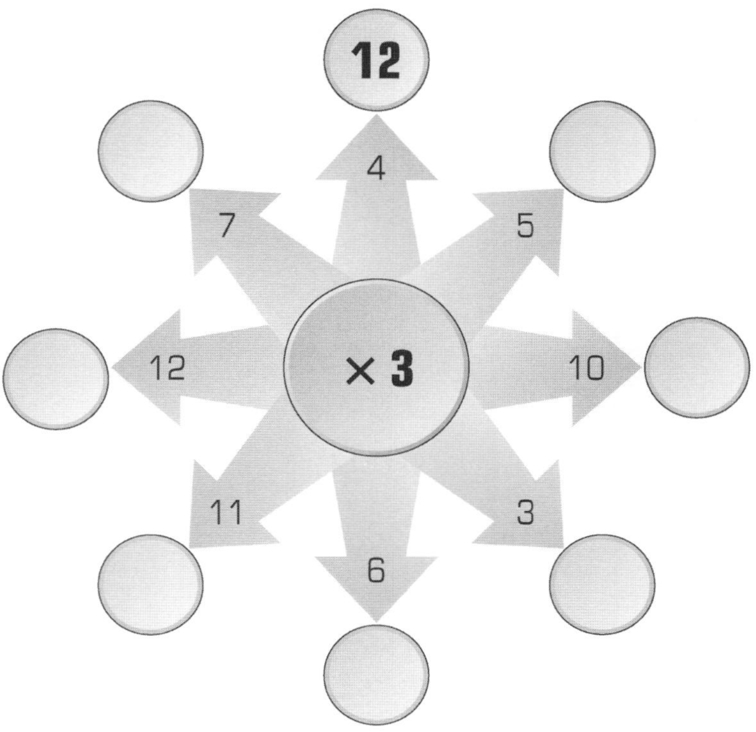

These are all multiples of 3.

2 Multiply the numbers in the arrow boxes by 4.

Write your answers in the circles.

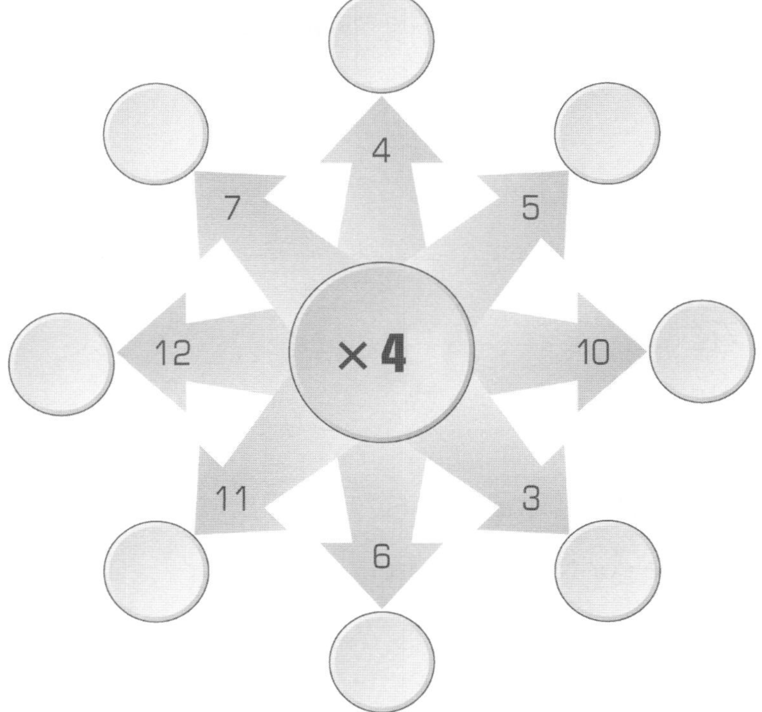

These are all multiples of 4.

10d Coordinates

Franco goes on a journey. Here is a map of the area.

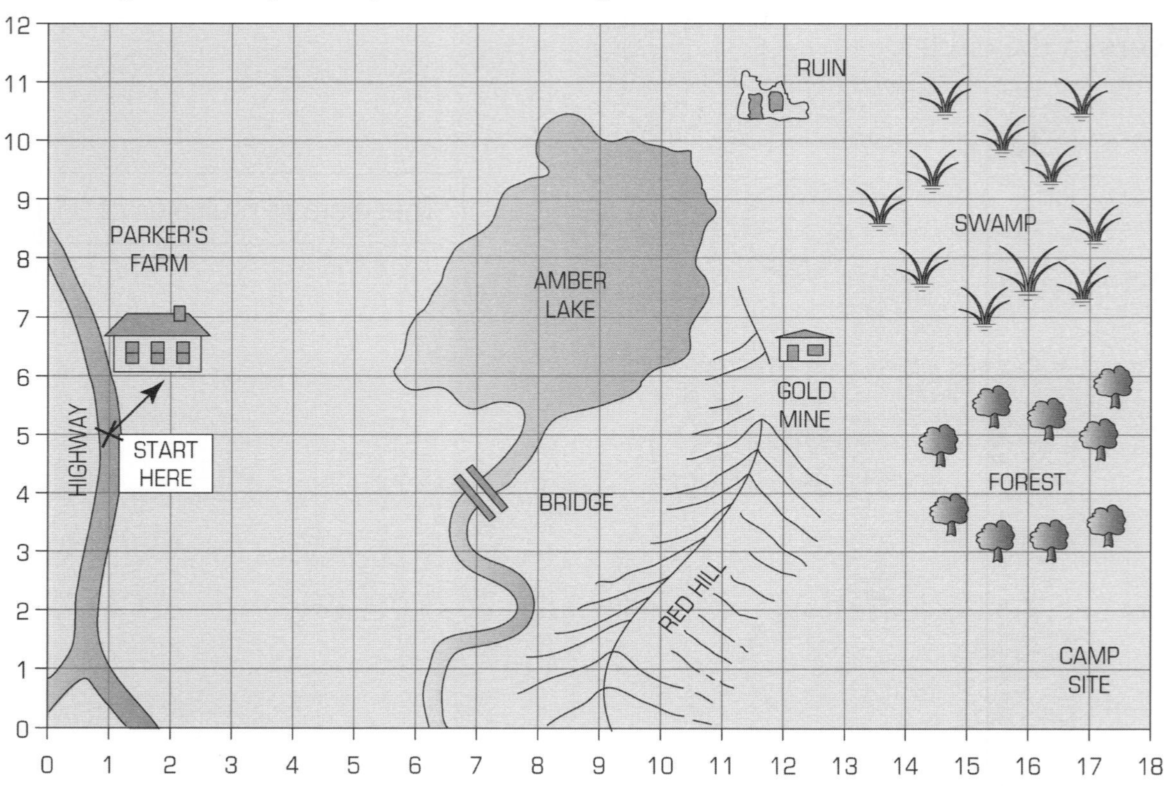

1 Plot the points and join them on the map to show Franco's journey.

(1, 5) (3, 7) (8, 11) (11, 10) (11, 8) (13, 7)

(14, 5) (14, 3) (15, 2) (17, 1)

Remember, you go **across** first, then up.

2 What will Franco see on his left at (3, 7)? ____________

3 What will Franco see on his right at (11, 10)? ____________

4 What will Franco see on his left at (11, 10)? ____________

5 What will Franco see on his right at (13, 7)? ____________

6 What will Franco see on his left at (15, 2)? ____________

7 Plot a shorter route from the Highway (1, 5) to the Camp Site (17, 1).

Draw the new route on the map, and write the coordinates here.

____

____

Coordinates and lines

I can do this page!

1 **a** Write the coordinates of the points A, B and C.

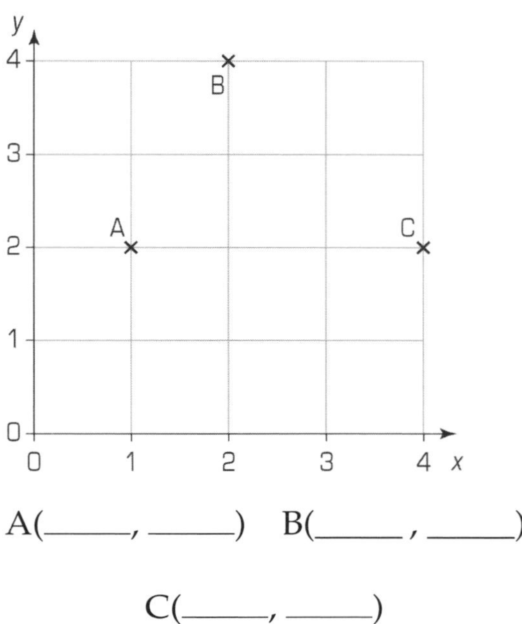

A(_____, _____) B(_____, _____)

C(_____, _____)

b Write the coordinates of the points P, Q and R.

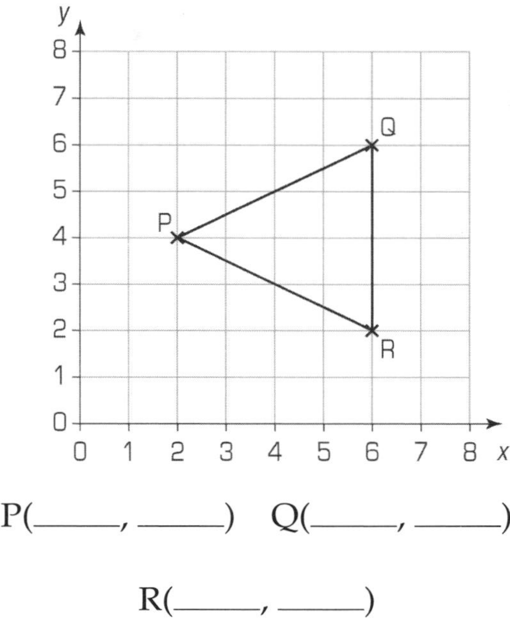

P(_____, _____) Q(_____, _____)

R(_____, _____)

2 **a** Plot these points on this grid.

(5, 3) (5, 6) (5, 9) (1, 6) (14, 6)

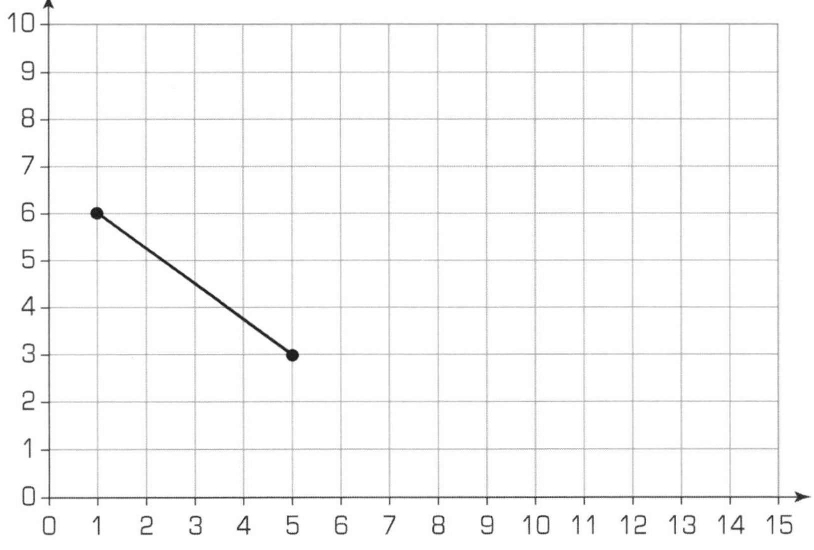

b Join all the points together, in order, with straight lines.

c What shape have you drawn? ____________

Reading graphs

I can do this page!

1 a Write coordinate pairs from this mapping.

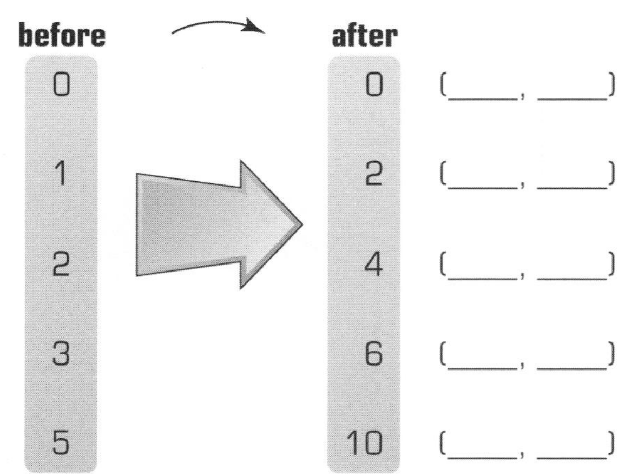

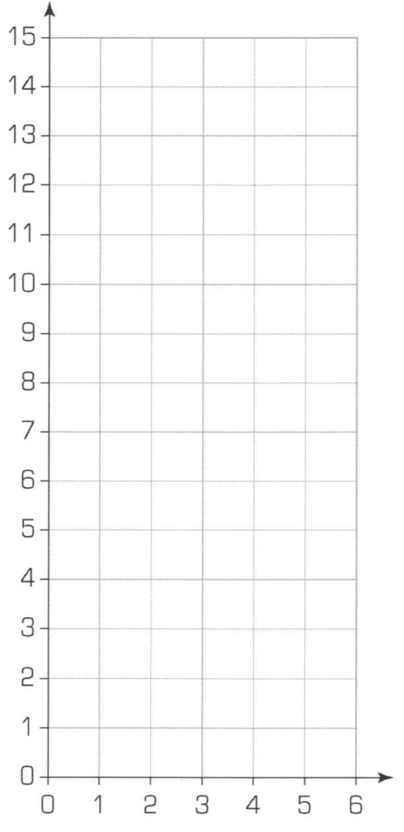

b Plot the points on this grid.

c Join the points with a straight line.

Use a ruler.

d Write the rule that connects the **before** and **after** numbers.

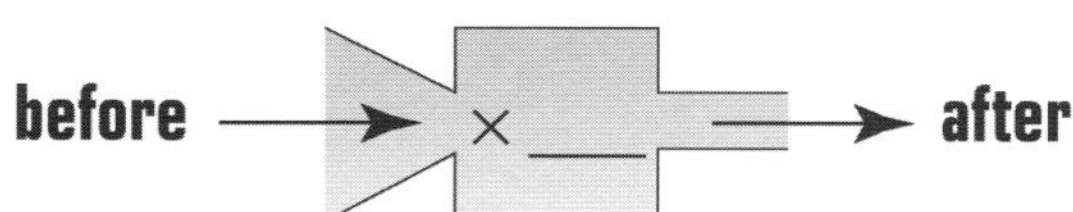

e Fill in these coordinate pairs from the graph:

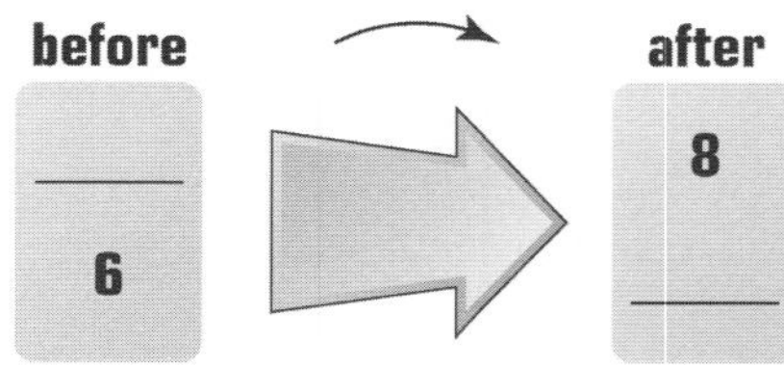

2 a Complete the mapping by filling in the **after** values from the graph.

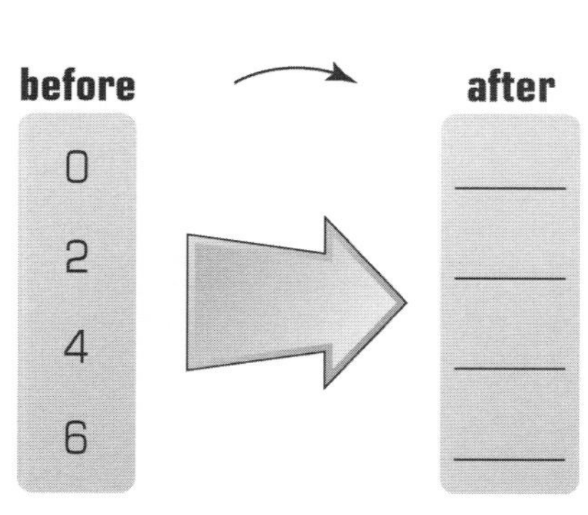

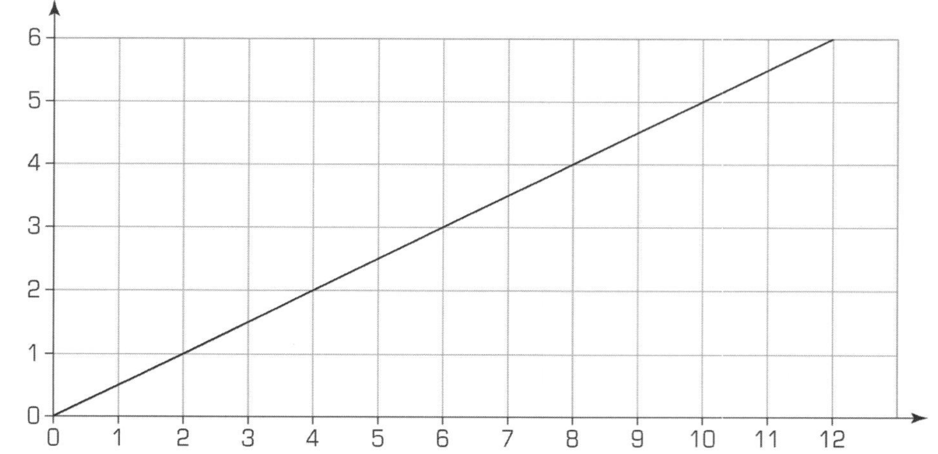

b What is the rule?

____

11a Fractions and divison

I can do this page!

1 Here are 10 cubes. Put them in two equal groups.

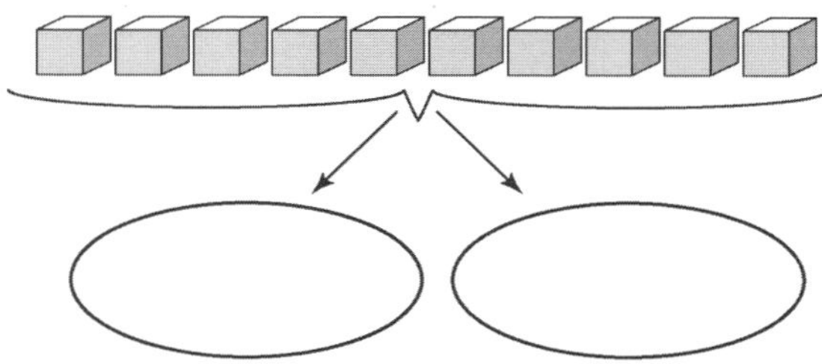

What is $\frac{1}{2}$ of 10?

Answer: ____

2 Here are 15 counters. Put them in three equal groups.

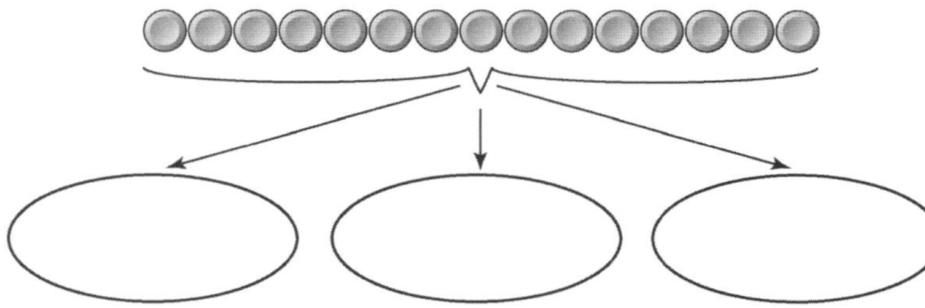

What is $\frac{1}{3}$ of 15?

Answer: ____

3 Which division goes with each calculation?

Draw arrows to connect them.

Calculation	division
$\frac{1}{4}$ of ____	$\div 2$
$\frac{1}{3}$ of ____	$\div 6$
$\frac{1}{8}$ of ____	$\div 4$
$\frac{1}{6}$ of ____	$\div 5$
$\frac{1}{2}$ of ____	$\div 10$
$\frac{1}{10}$ of ____	$\div 8$
$\frac{1}{5}$ of ____	$\div 3$

For example:

$\frac{1}{4}$ of 12 means $12 \div 4 = 3$

11b Fractions of a quantity

1 Use the multiplication grid to help you find:

×	1	2	3	4	5	6
1	1	2	3	4	5	6
2	2	4	6	8	10	12
3	3	6	9	12	15	18
4	4	8	12	16	20	24
5	5	10	15	20	25	30
6	6	12	18	24	30	36

a $\frac{1}{2}$ of 8 = ______ **b** $\frac{1}{3}$ of 9 = ______

c $\frac{1}{4}$ of 16 = ______ **d** $\frac{1}{5}$ of 15 = ______

e $\frac{1}{3}$ of 18 = ______ **f** $\frac{1}{4}$ of 24 = ______

g $\frac{1}{6}$ of 24 = ______ **h** $\frac{1}{2}$ of 12 = ______

i $\frac{1}{5}$ of 30 = ______ **j** $\frac{1}{6}$ of 30 = ______

2 Find:

a $\frac{1}{2}$ of 18 = ______ **b** $\frac{1}{2}$ of 24 = ______ **c** $\frac{1}{2}$ of 40 = ______

3 Find:

a $\frac{1}{4}$ of 28 = ______ **b** $\frac{1}{4}$ of 40 = ______ **c** $\frac{1}{4}$ of 32 = ______

4 Find:

a $\frac{1}{3}$ of 24 = ______ **b** $\frac{1}{3}$ of 30 = ______ **c** $\frac{1}{3}$ of 36 = ______

5 Use the machines to find these fractions of amounts.

a $\frac{3}{4}$ of 12

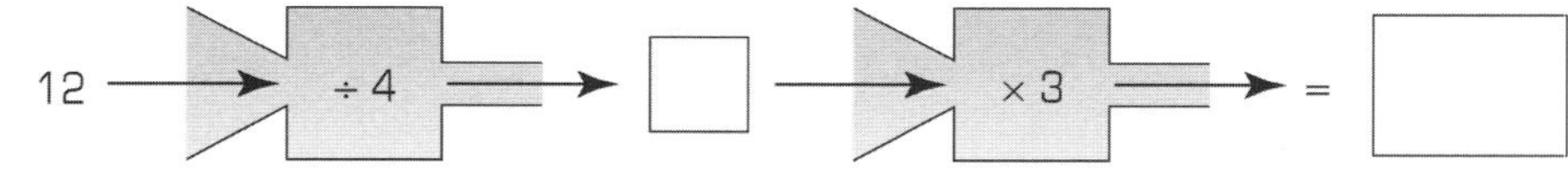

b $\frac{3}{4}$ of 20

20 → ÷ 4 → ☐ → × 3 → = ☐

c $\frac{2}{3}$ of 15

15 → ÷ 3 → ☐ → × 2 → = ☐

Percentages

I can do this page!

1 Here are 20 counters: 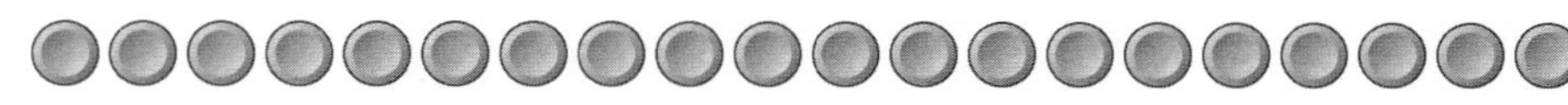

Share them equally into the percentage strip.

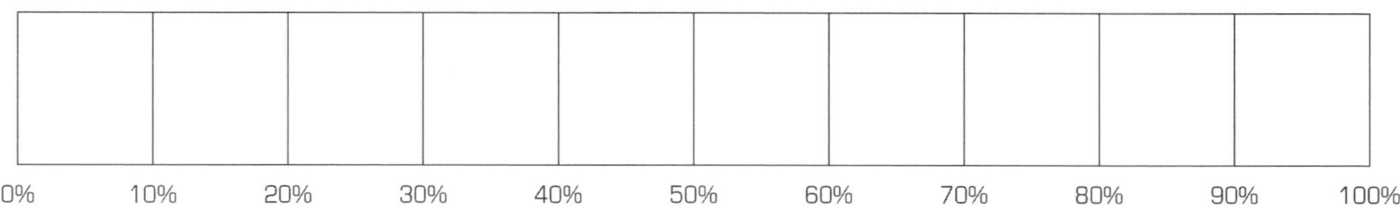

Use the strip to work out:

a 50% of 20 counters = ______

b 10% of 20 counters = ______

c 30% of 20 counters = ______

d 80% of 20 counters = ______

2 A pizza is cut into 10 equal slices. Each slice is 10% of the whole pizza.

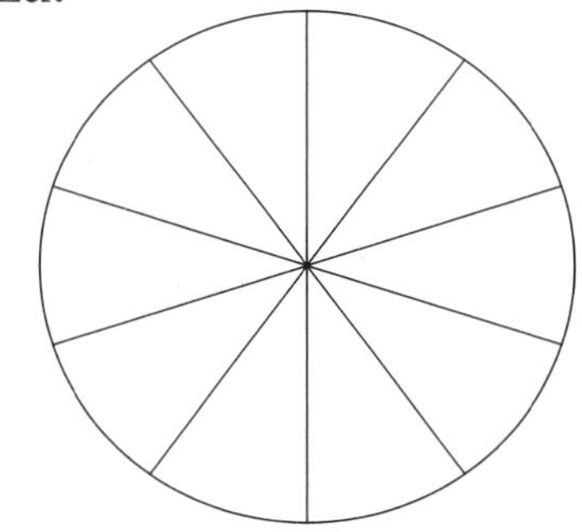

a Colour 3 slices blue. What percentage is this? __________%

b Colour 3 slices green. What percentage is this? __________%

c Colour 3 slices red. What percentage is this? __________%

d What percentage of the pizza is left? __________%

3 Here are 50 counters:

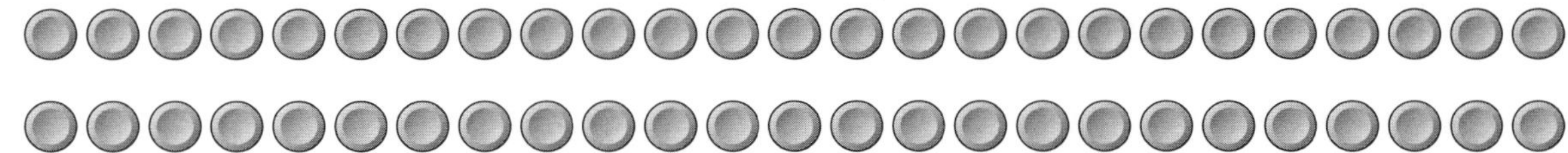

Share them equally into the percentage strip.

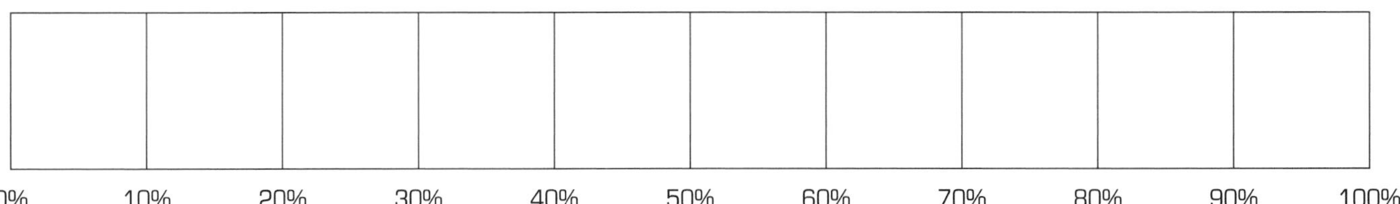

Use the strip to work out:

a 10% of 50 counters = ______

b 30% of 50 counters = ______

c 50% of 50 counters = ______

d 80% of 50 counters = ______

11d Ratio and proportion

1 a Colour 4 of these tins red and 3 tins blue.

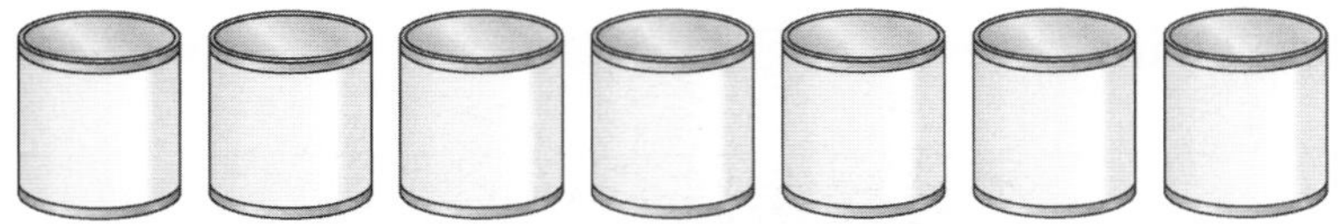

b What is the ratio of red to blue? _____ : _____

2 a Colour 3 of these tins red and 6 tins blue.

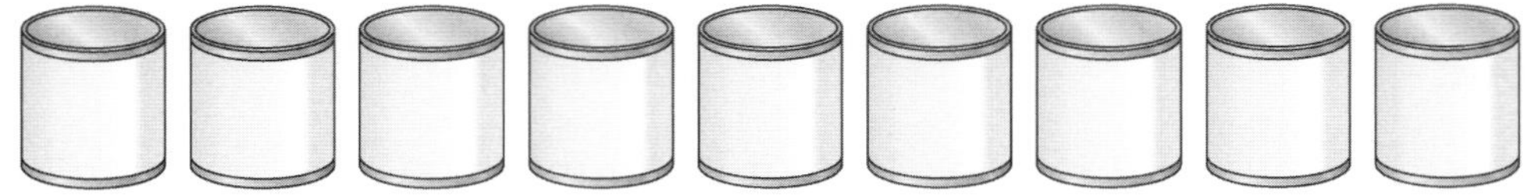

b What is the ratio of red to blue? _____ : _____

3 What is the ratio of blue beads to white beads on these strings?

a _____ : _____

b _____ : _____

c _____ : _____

d _____ : _____

4 This string of beads is made up from blue and white beads in the ratio of 1 : 4.

Colour in the string of beads.

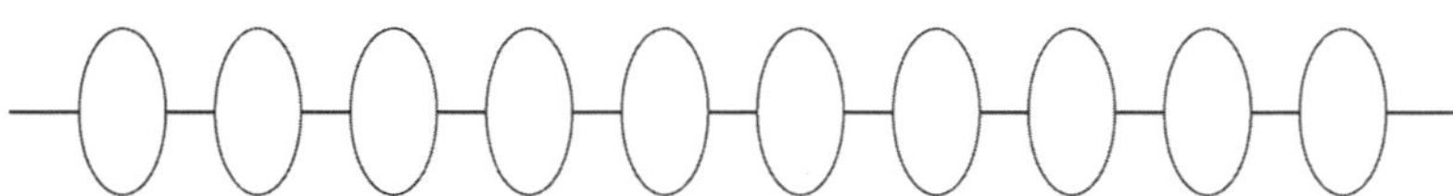

5 In this string the ratio of blue beads to white beads is 3 : 2.

Colour in this string of beads.

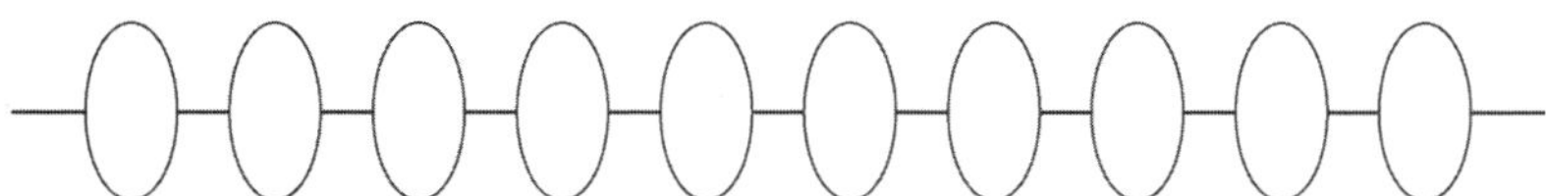

6 The ratio of blue beads to white beads on a string is 2 : 1.

There are 10 blue beads.

How many white beads are needed? _____

12a Using symbols

1 Ravi has n apples.

Toby has 7 more apples than Ravi.

How many does Toby have?

Toby has $n + 7$ apples.

Jenny has 3 more apples than Ravi.

How many does Jenny have?

Jenny has _____ apples.

2 Tom, Jade and Eva all had the same number of sweets.

Tom ate 5 sweets so he had $n - 5$ sweets left.

Jade ate 3 sweets so she had _____ sweets left.

Eva ate 6 sweets so she had _____ sweets left.

3 The Jones family had a chocolate bar with n pieces.

Dad ate 3 pieces leaving $n - 3$.

Mum ate 2 pieces leaving $n - 3 - 2$ or $n - 5$.

Clare ate 5 pieces leaving _____ or _____.

Paul ate 3 pieces leaving _____ or _____.

12b Adding with symbols

I can do this page!

Number towers

Add the numbers in two boxes next to each other to get the number in the box below.

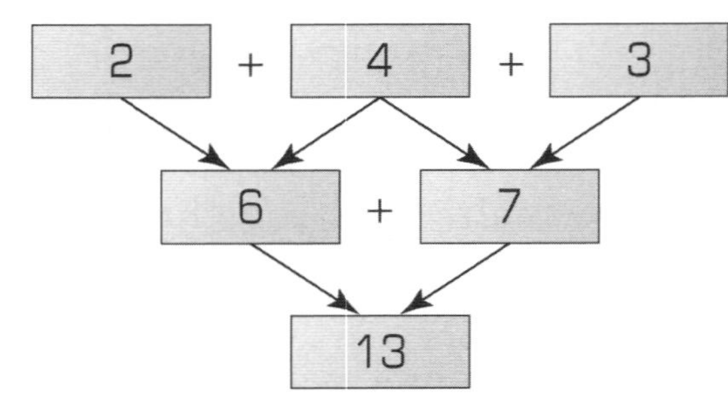

Complete these towers.

1
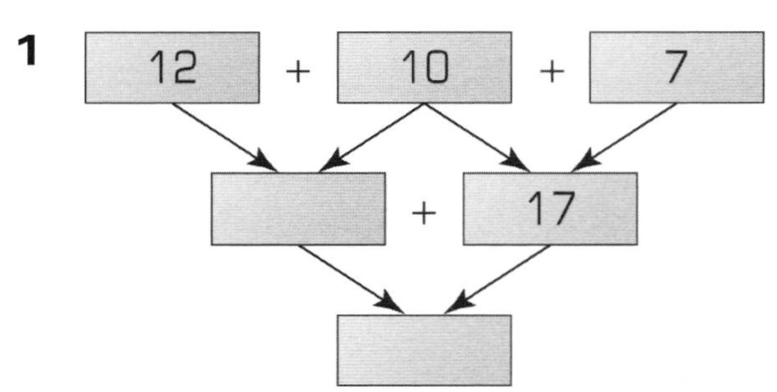

2
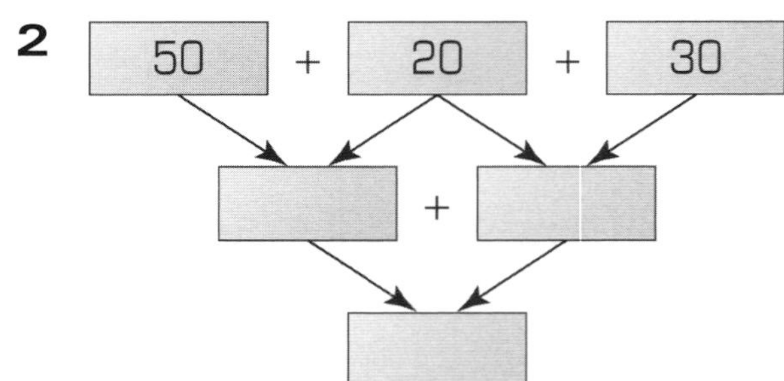

3
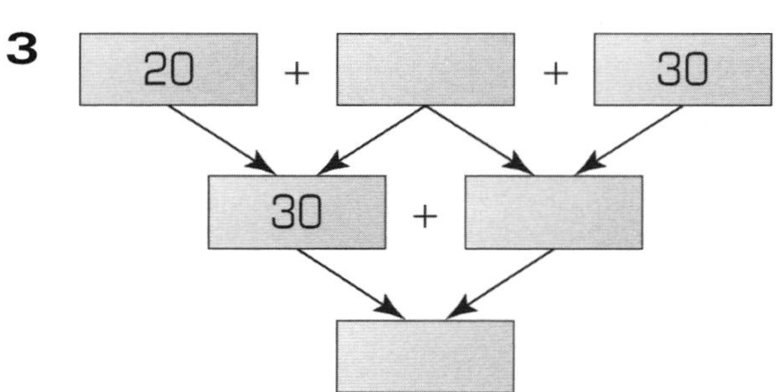

4
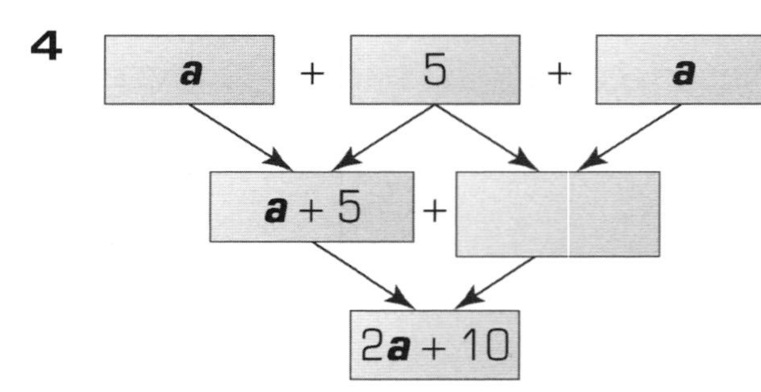

5
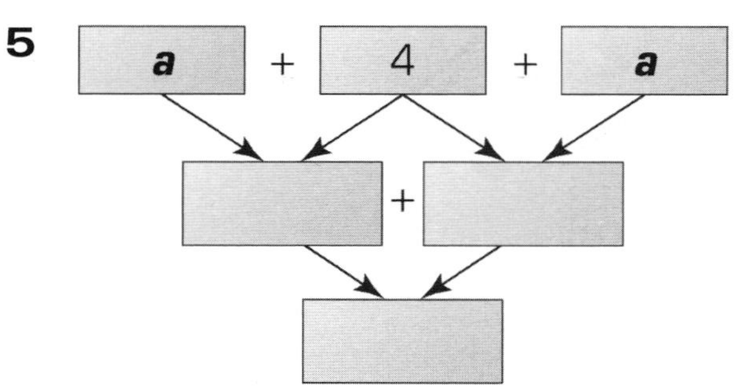

6
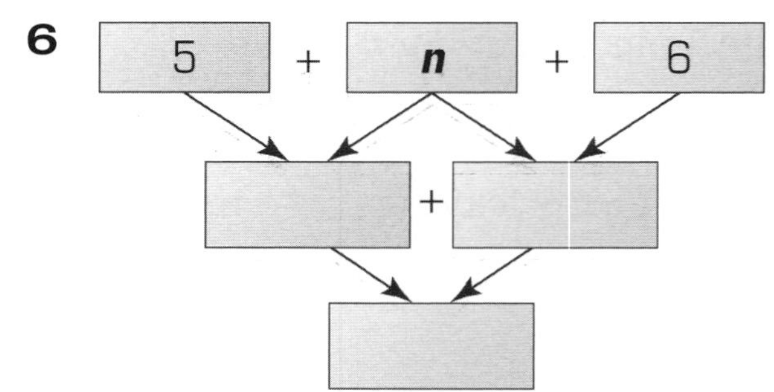

12c Simplifying symbols

1 How many of each symbol are in the box?

Write the numbers in the boxes below.

$\square\, a + \square\, g + \square\, k$

a	k	g	a	a
k	k	g	g	
a	a	a	g	a
k	a	g	a	g

2 How many a symbols are in each line?

Write the number in the space.

The first one is done for you

a $b + a + 2a =$ <u>3</u> $a + b$

b $4a + 2a - b =$ ____ $a - b$

c $6a - a + 3b =$ ____ $a + 3b$

d $2a + 2a + 2b =$ ____ $a + 2b$

e $5b + a + 3a =$ ____ $a + 5b$

f $2a + 3b + 3b - a =$ ____ $a + 3b$

3 How many of each symbol are in each line?

Write the numbers in the spaces.

The first one is done for you

a $5p + 4r - r =$ <u>5</u> $p +$ <u>3</u> r

b $8n + 3n + 6t =$ ____ $n +$ ____ t

c $2a + a + 3b + b =$ ____ $a +$ ____ b

d $2g + 3s + 2g + 3s =$ ____ $g +$ ____ s

e $6c - c + 3d - d =$ ____ $c +$ ____ d

Maths Life

Media Maths

I can do this page!

Angela needs to be active 300 minutes per week. Add the times in her diary to see if she makes her goal.

The Newspaper | Monday 11 May 2009

MAY 2009

Monday, 4 May
Walk to/from school 20 minutes
Take dog to the park 60 minutes

Tuesday, 5 May 2009
Walk to/from school 20 minutes
PE 40 minutes
Swim 60 minutes

Wednesday, 6 May 2009
Walk to/from school 20 minutes

MAY

Thursday, 7 May 2009
Walk to/from school 20 minut
PE 40 minute
Take dog to the park 60 minute

Friday, 8 May 2009
Walk to/from school 20 minutes

Saturday, 9 May 2009
Cricket 80 minutes

Sunday, 10 May 2009
Cycle ride 60 minutes

Total active time = ______

On which activity does she spend the most time?

On which activity does she spend the least time?

13a Lines of symmetry

Draw all the lines of symmetry onto these shapes.

Remember to use a ruler.

1

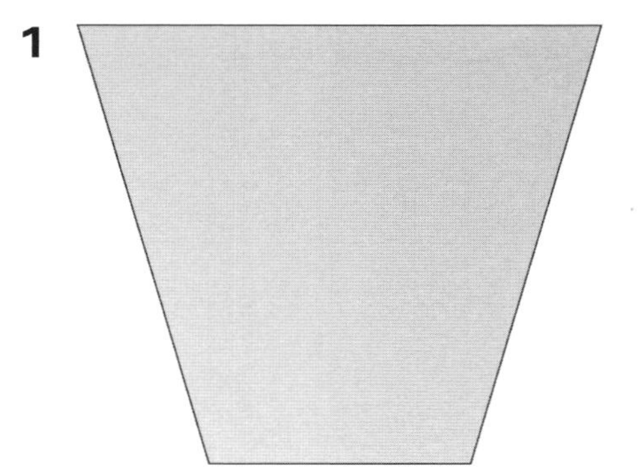

2

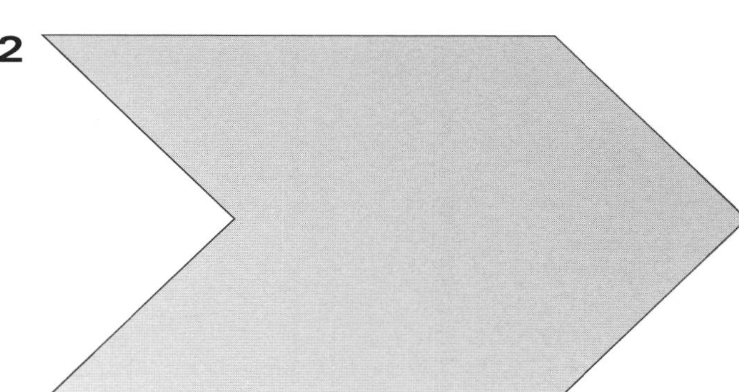

3

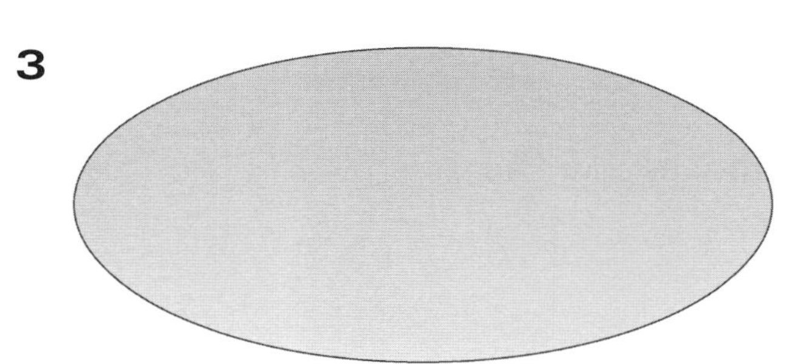

4

5

6

Reflection

I can do this page!

1 Draw the reflection of each shape in the mirror line.

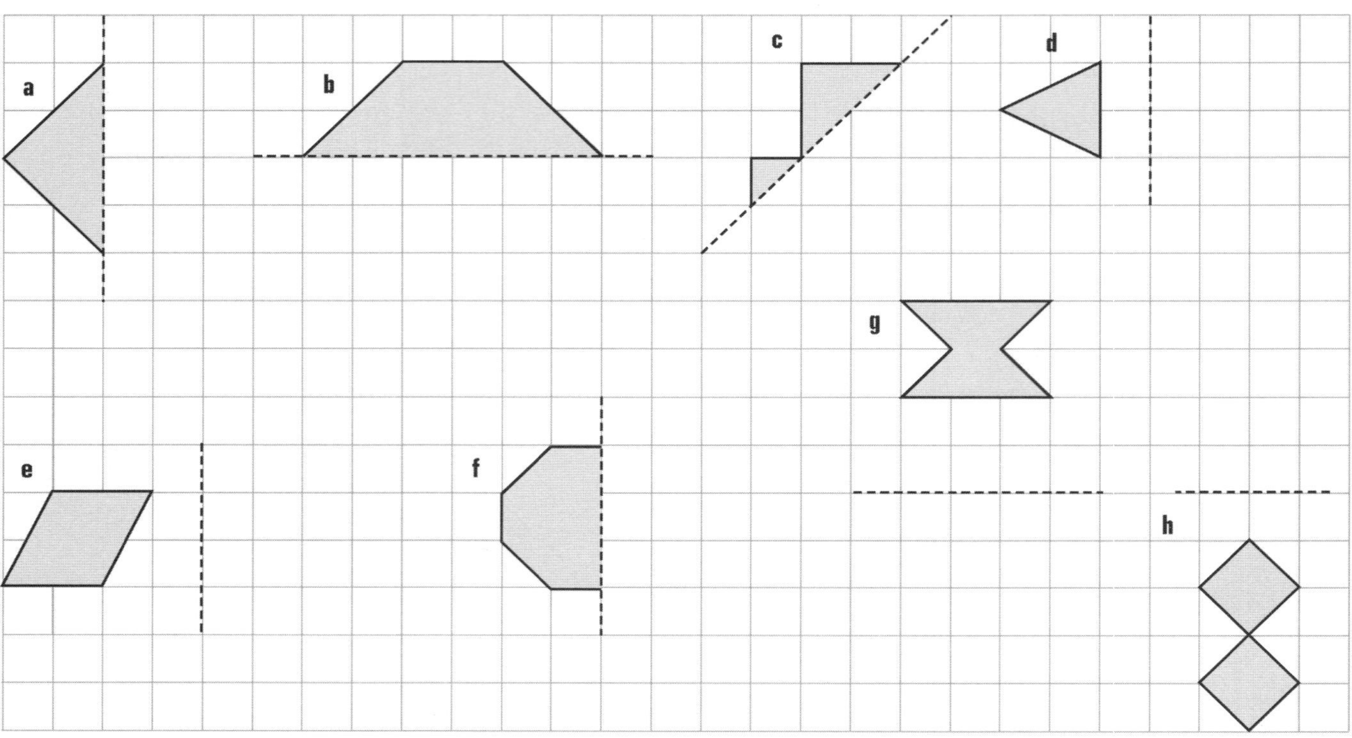

2 Reflect this drawing in the mirror line to complete the 'happy' face.

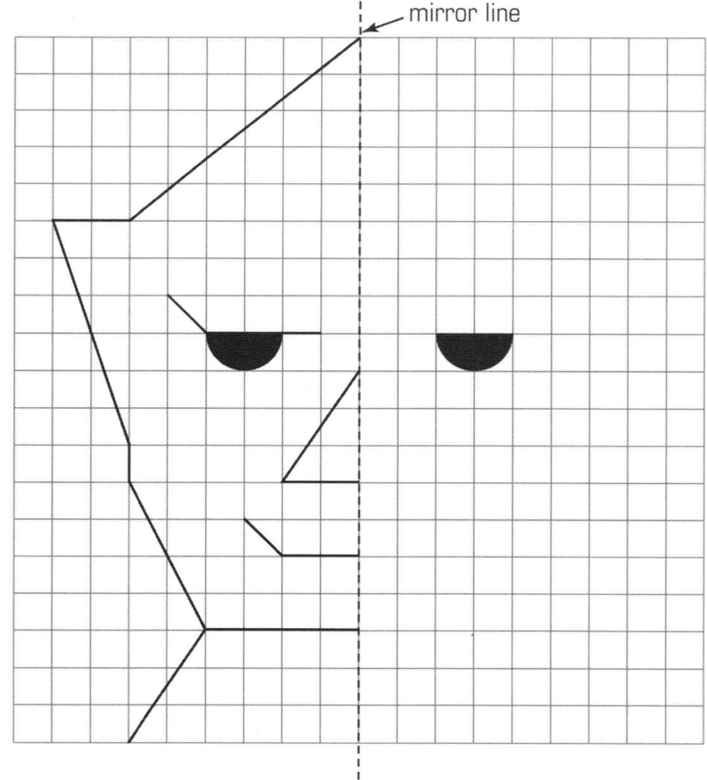

13c Translation

1 Use these instructions to translate each shape and draw its new position.

The first one is done for you

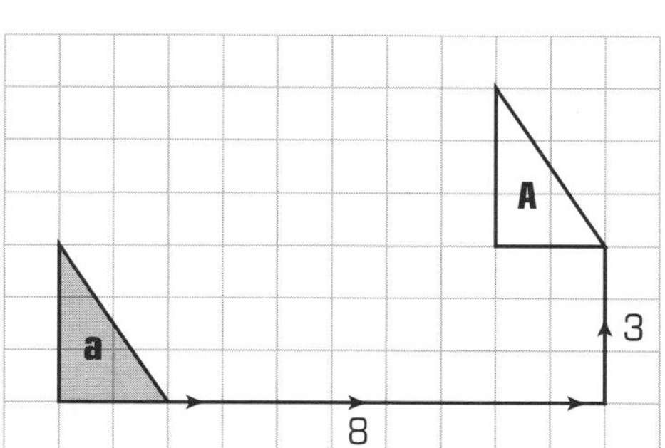

Shape **a**

8 right and 3 up

Shape **b**

5 right and 2 down

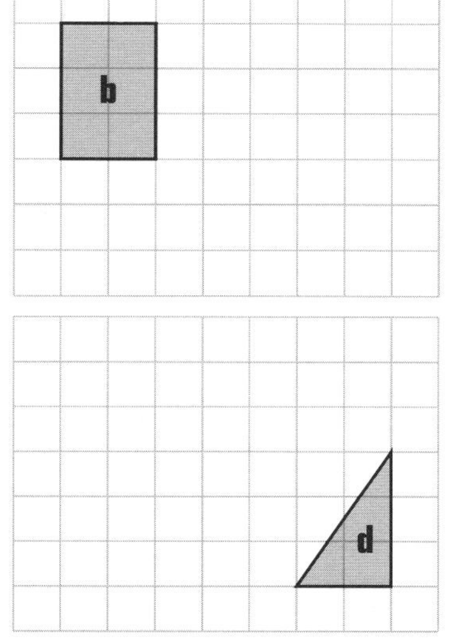

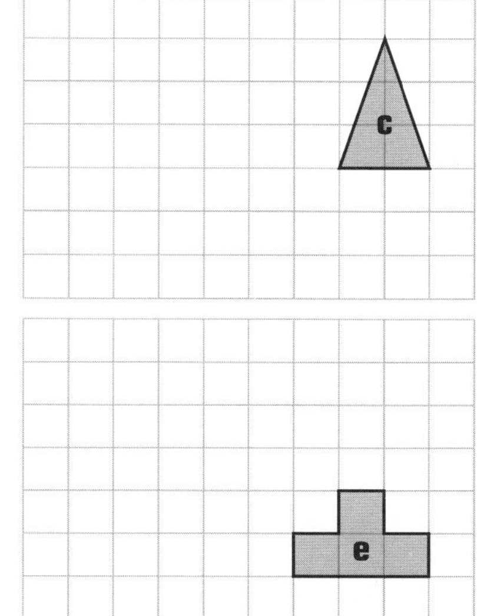

Shape **c**

5 left and 2 down

Shape **d**

5 left and 3 up

Shape **e**

2 left and 4 up

2 Describe the translation of each shape.

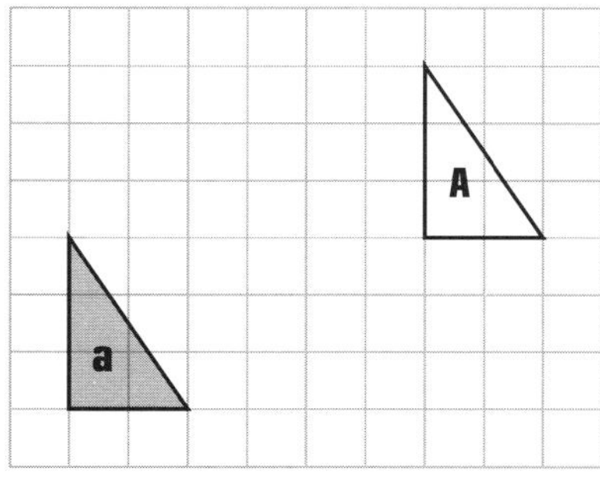

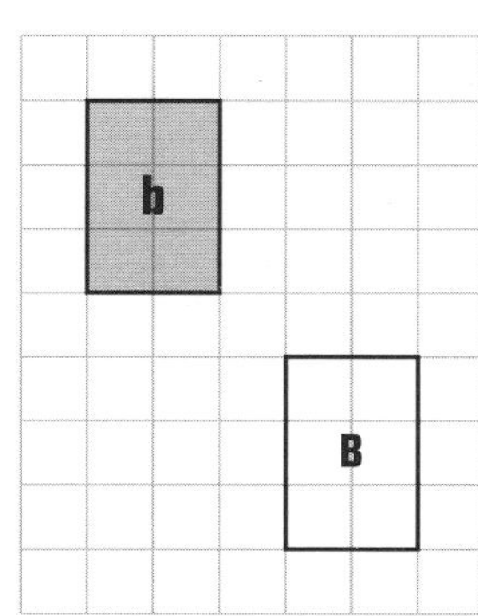

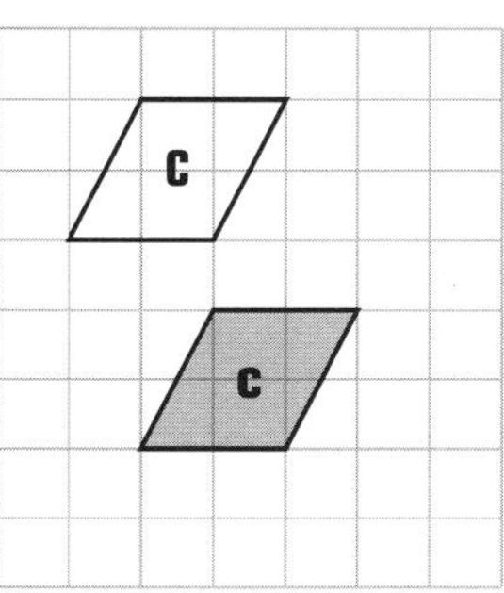

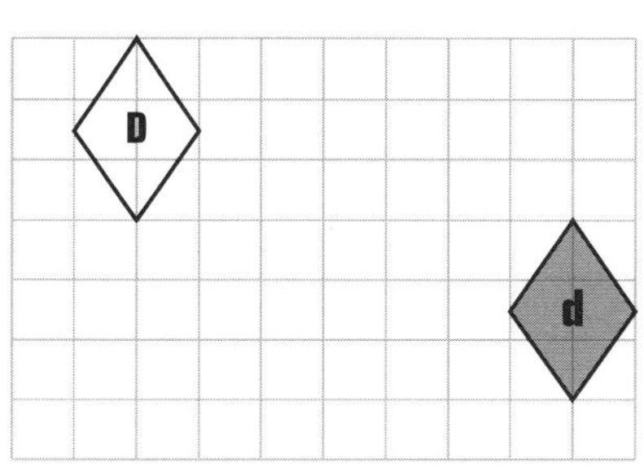

a to **A** 6 right and

_____ up

b to **B** 3 right and

_____ down

c to **C** ______________________

____

d to **D** ______________________

____

Count across first then up or down

13d Rotation

1 How many degrees are shown in these angles?

a

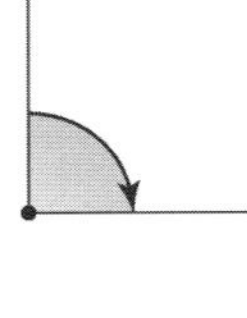

_____°

b

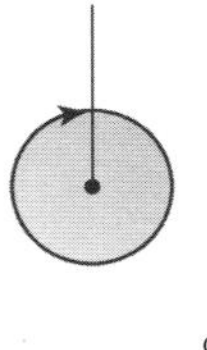

_____°

c

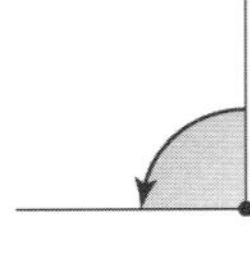

_____°

d

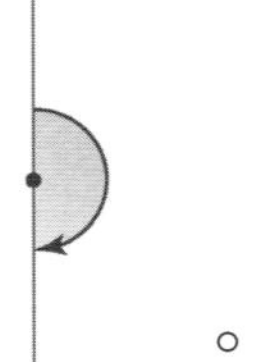

_____°

2 One wheel is turning clockwise and the other is turning anti-clockwise.

Label each wheel correctly.

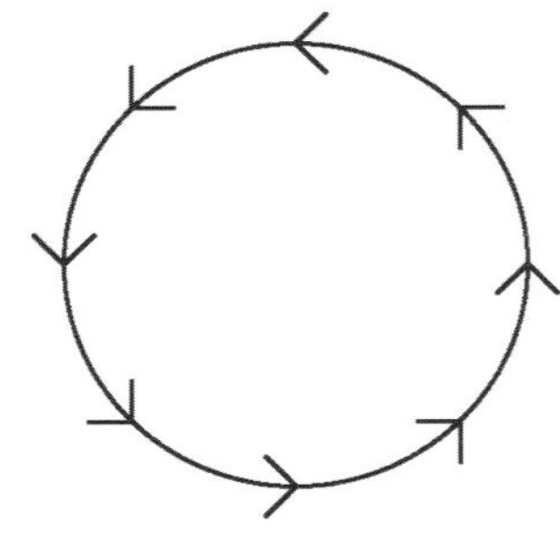

_______________ _______________

3 Rotate this shape through 180°.

Draw the new shape.

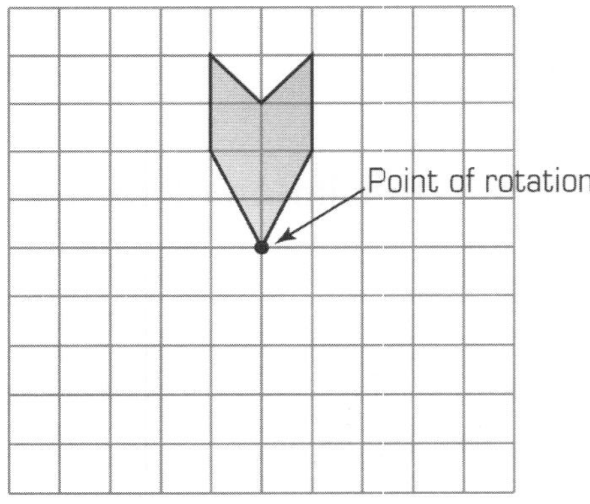

4 **a** Rotate this shape **A** through 90° clockwise.

Label the new shape **B**.

b Now, rotate the original shape **A** through 90° anti-clockwise.

Label the new shape **C**.

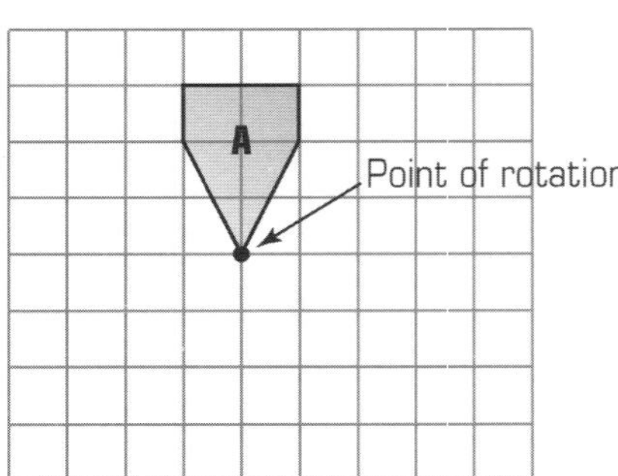

13f Tessellations

1 Tessellate this shape 15 times on the grid.

It must fit together with no gaps or overlaps.

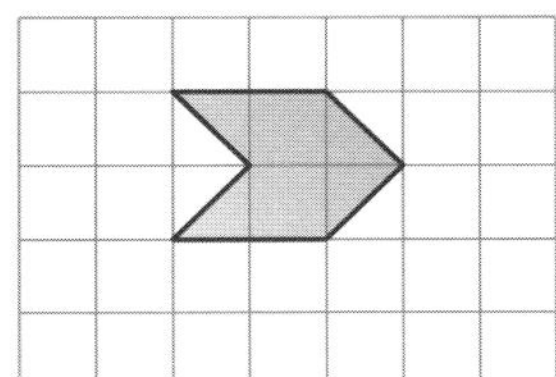

2 Which of these shapes will tessellate? Use the grid to test each shape.

If the shape tessellates, put a tick (✔) inside it.

a

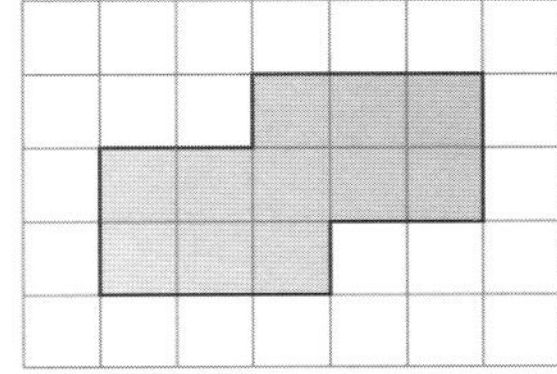

b

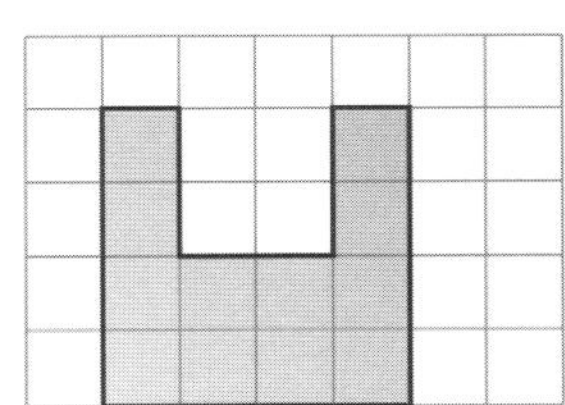

c

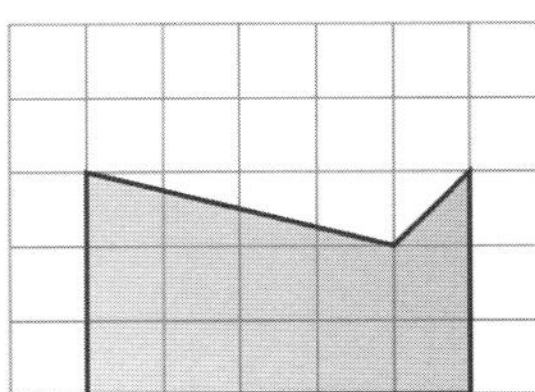

d

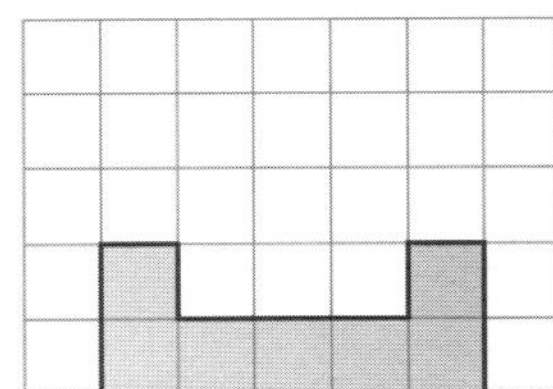

e

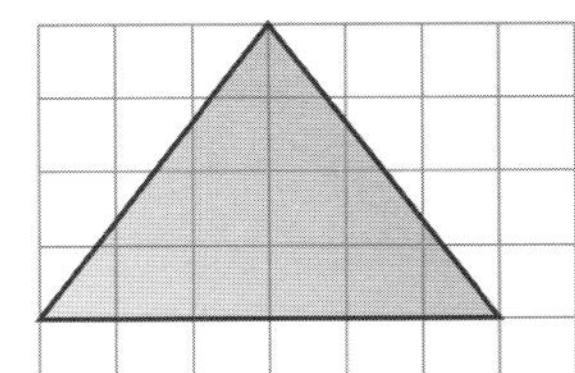

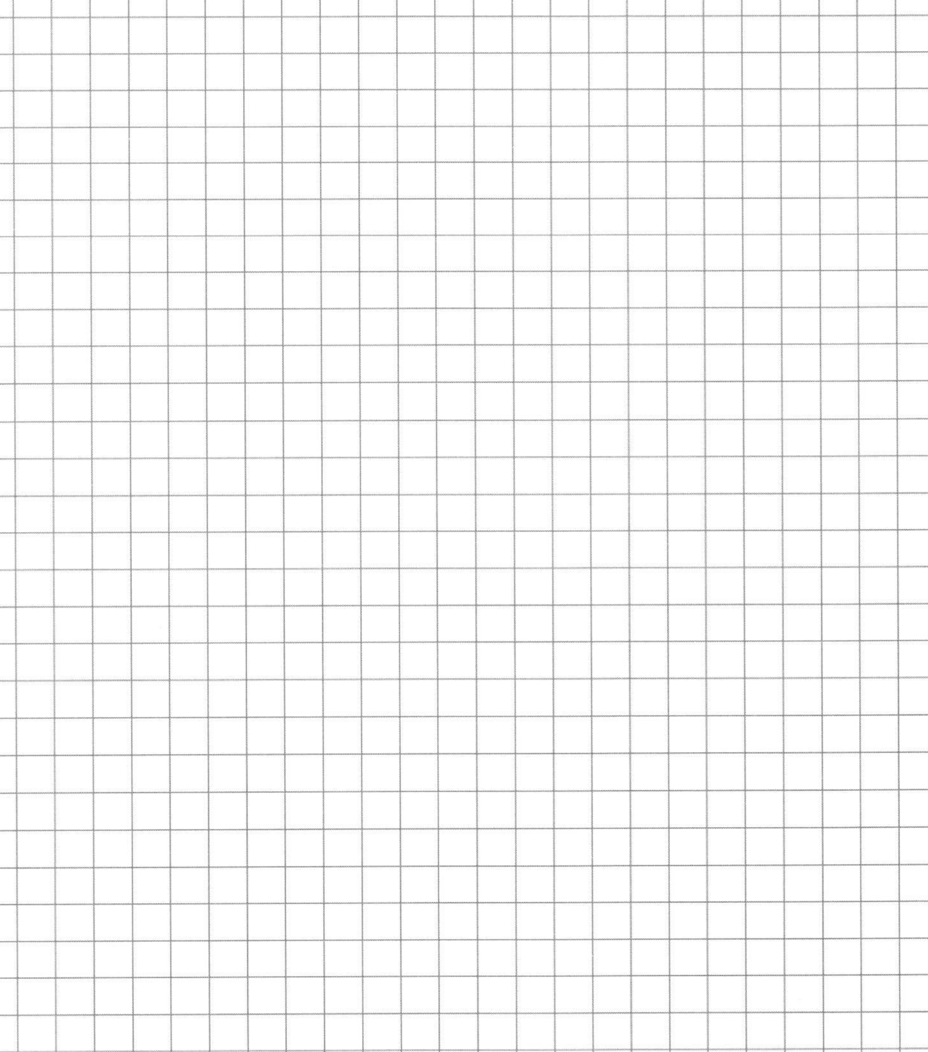

14c More bar charts

I can do this page!

1 How much does each 'tally' show?

The first is done for you.

a 卌 II = 7 **b** 卌 卌 = ______ **c** 卌 卌 IIII = ______ **d** 卌 卌 卌
卌 卌 II = ______

2 Show these numbers as a tally.

a 9 = ____________ **b** 12 = ____________

c 15 = ____________ **d** 23 = ____________

3 Class 7M do a survey of hair colour in their class.

Brown	Red	Brown	~~Black~~	Blonde	Brown	Blonde
~~Black~~	Blonde	Brown	~~Black~~	~~Black~~	Brown	
Blonde	Brown	Brown	Red	Blonde	~~Black~~	Blonde

a Complete this tally of the data.

b Complete this bar chart using the data from the tally chart.

Colour	Tally	Frequency
Black	卌	5
Blonde		
Brown		
Red		

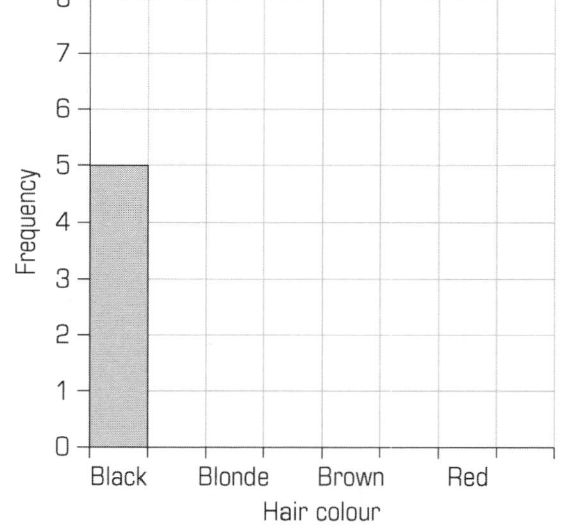

c What is the biggest group?

Answer: ____________.

14d Mode

1 This bar chart shows the number of books sold in the book shop on Monday.

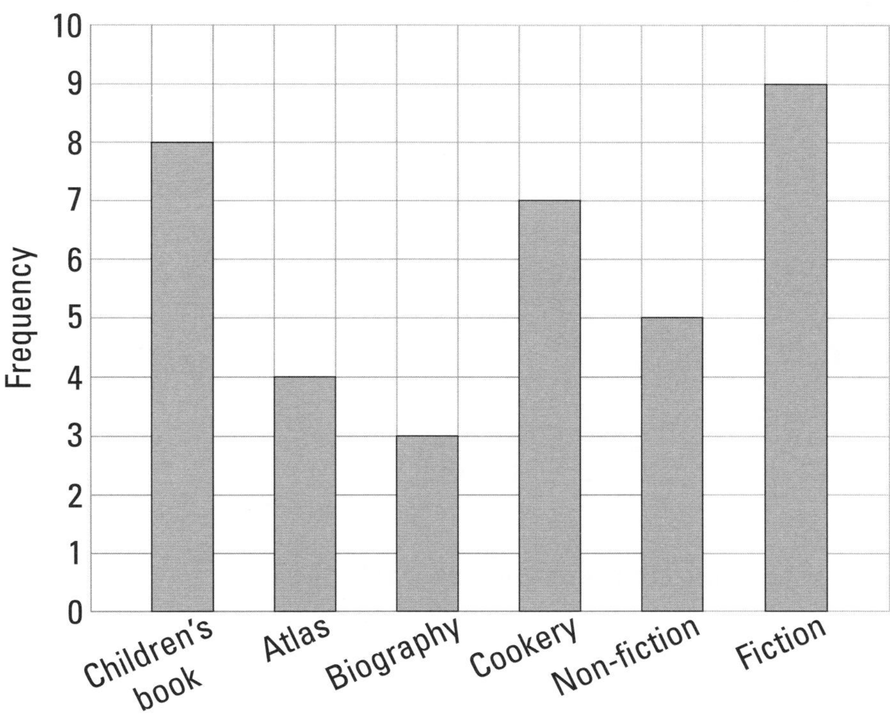

a Put the books in order of sales starting with the **fewest** sold.

Biography, Atlas, ___________________________

b How many cookery books were sold? ___________________________

c How many children's books were sold? ___________________________

d How many atlases were sold? ___________________________

e How many more children's books than atlases were sold? ___________________________

f What was the **least** popular type of book sold? ___________________________

g Which type of book was the **most** popular? ___________________________

h The **mode** is the type of book that was most popular. That is ___________________________

14e The range

I can do this page!

1 What is the range of the number of items?

a

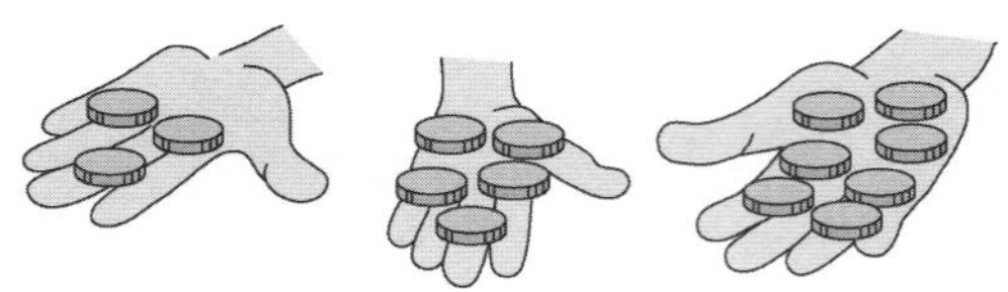

_____ coins

b

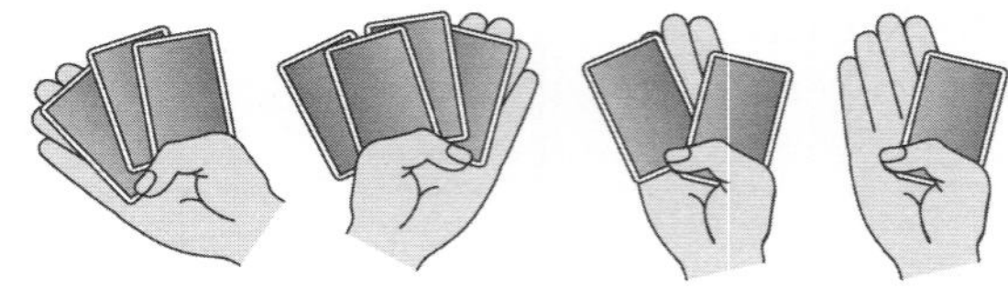

_____ cards

c

_____ pencils

d

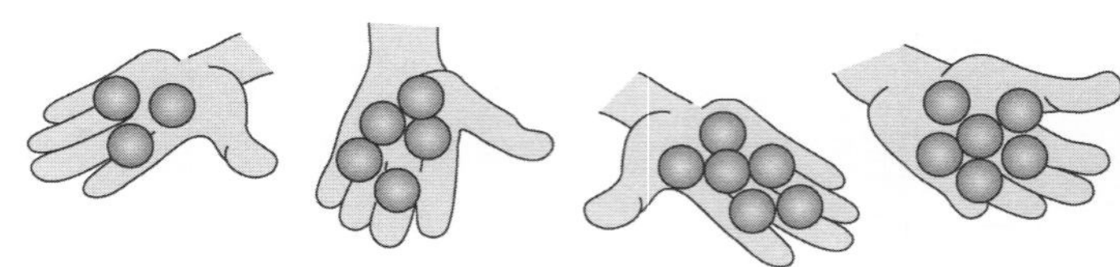

_____ sweets

2 Maya took a survey of the colour of teacher's cars in the car park.

Colour	Tally	Frequency
Red	卌 卌 III	
Blue	卌 I	
Green	卌 II	
Silver	卌 卌 卌 IIII	
Brown	II	
Black	卌	
White	IIII	

a Fill in the frequencies.

b How many cars are there in the car park altogether? ______________________

c The **mode** is the most common value. The mode is ______________________

d What is the **range** of the number of cars for each colour? ______________________

14f Comparing data sets

These are the average temperatures each month for London and Wick.

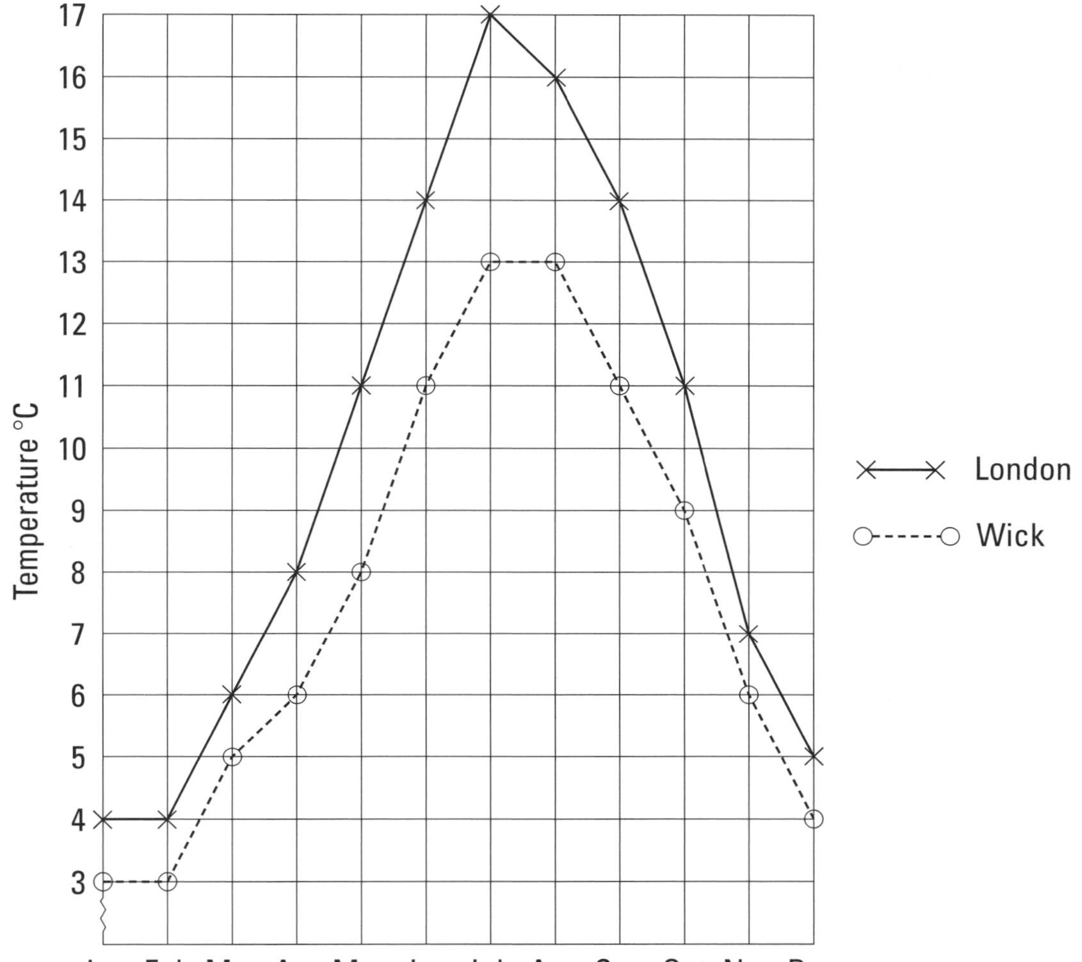

1 Does the line like this ×——× represent London or Wick? ______

2 What does the Wick line look like? ______

3 Why are there 12 points on the graph for each city? ______

4 What is the temperature range? ______

5 Which city had the highest temperature in July? ______

6 What was the highest July temperature? ______

7 What was the average Wick temperature in March? ______

8 What is the difference in temperatures in May? ______

9 What is the difference in temperatures in July? ______

15b Mental addition and subtraction

Fill in the squares with the correct numbers and operations.

1

8	+	5	=	
−		−		−
	+		=	8
=		=		=
		1	=	

2

6	+	5	=	
4	+		=	5
=		=		=
		4	=	6

3

	+	3	=	10
		−		+
8	−		=	
=		=		=
	+		=	16

15f Written methods of multiplication

1 Split up these numbers into hundreds, tens and units.

For example: 163 = 100 + 60 + 3

a 175 = _____ + _____ + _____

b 98 = _____ + _____

c 209 = _____ + _____

d 530 = _____ + _____

2 Use these grids to complete these multiplications.

a $32 \times 3 =$ _____

×	30	2
3		

b $43 \times 4 =$ _____

×	40	3
4		

c $65 \times 6 =$ _____

×	60	5
6		

d $28 \times 7 =$ _____

×	20	8
7		

e $92 \times 4 =$ _____

×		

f $54 \times 7 =$ _____

×		

g $124 \times 3 =$ _____

×	100	20	4
3			

h $136 \times 3 =$ _____

×			

15g Written methods of division

Fill in the spaces to help you complete the divisions.

1 93 ÷ 3

```
    9 3
 −  3 0    ←  3 × 10
    6 3
 − [   ]   ←  3 × 10
   [   ]
 − [   ]   ←  3 × 10
     [ ]
 −   [ ]   ←  3 × 1
```

93 ÷ 3 = [   ]

2 192 ÷ 6

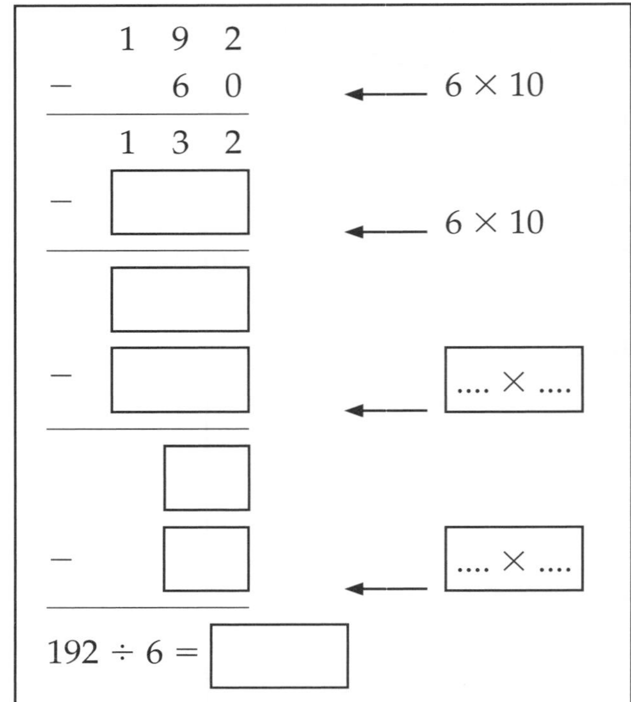

3 108 ÷ 9

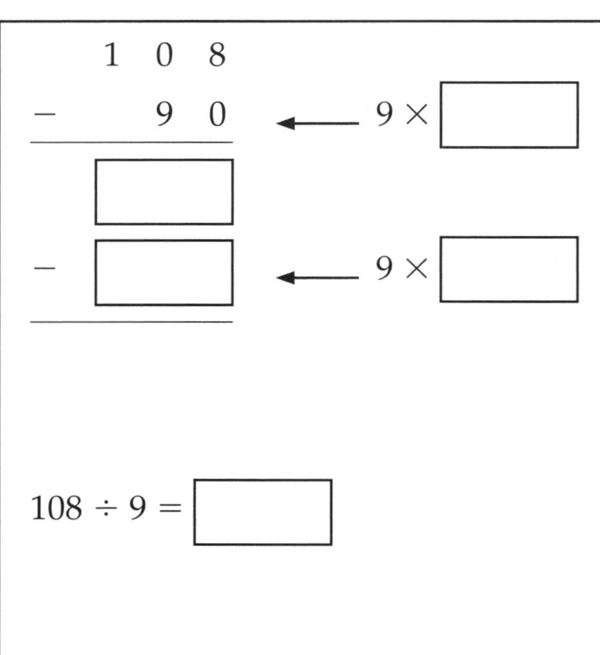

4 92 ÷ 4

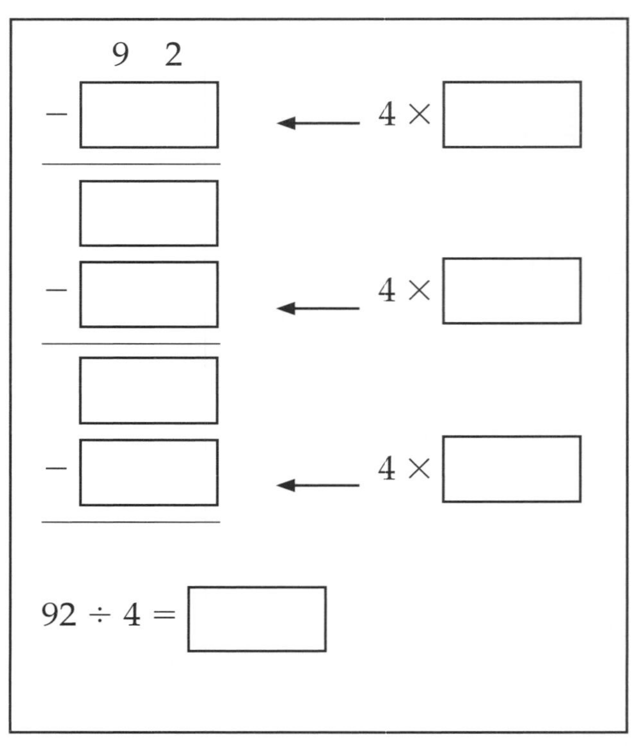

15h Finding a percentage

1 Here are 20 beads.

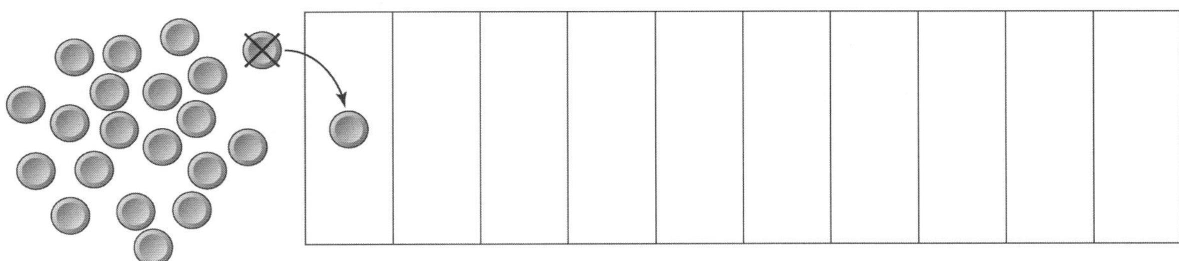

a Share the beads equally between the 10 sections.

Each section is 10% or $\frac{1}{10}$.

b Use the drawing to link these calculations to their correct answers. The first one is done for you.

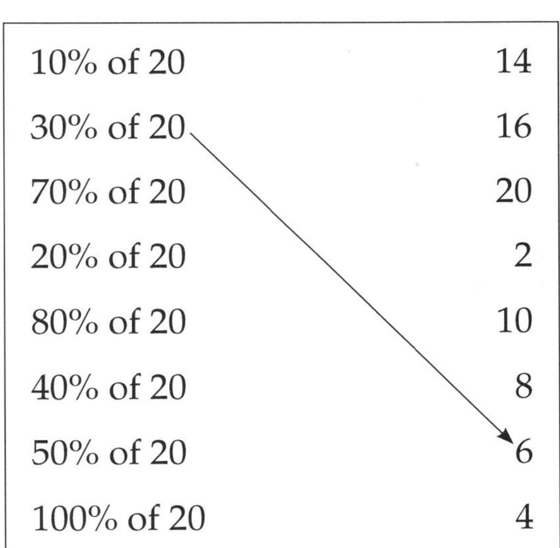

10% of 20	14
30% of 20	16
70% of 20	20
20% of 20	2
80% of 20	10
40% of 20	8
50% of 20	6
100% of 20	4

2 This plank measures 10 cm.

10%

a Divide the plank into exactly 10% sections. The first one has been done for you.

b 10% of the plank has been shaded. Shade another 40%.

c How much of the plank is now shaded? Answer: _____%

3 a Shade 60% of this rectangle.

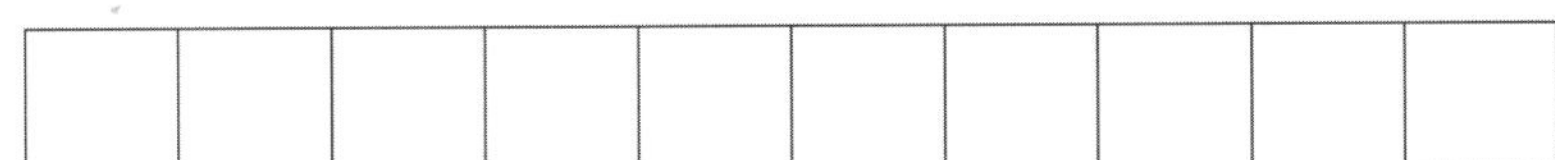

b Use the diagram in question 1 to find 60% of 20. Answer: _____

15i Solving problems

The perimeter of a shape is the total distance around the edge.

This triangle has sides of 4 cm.

Its perimeter is 4 cm + 4 cm + 4 cm = 12 cm

You can say: 3×4 cm = 12 cm.

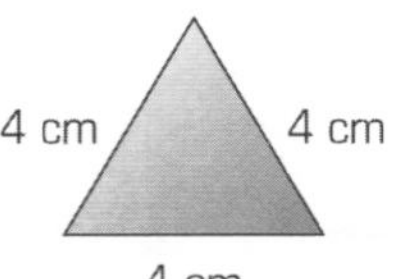

1 Find the perimeter of these shapes.

a

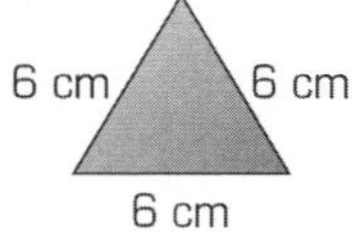

The perimeter is:

_____ cm + _____ cm + _____ cm

= _____ cm

Or:

_____ × _____ cm = _____ cm

b

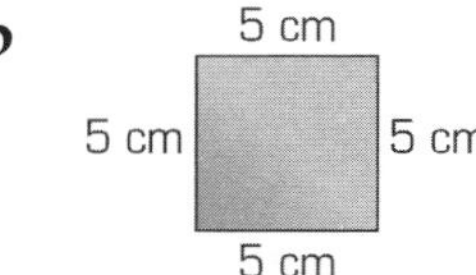

The perimeter is:

_____ cm + _____ cm + _____ cm + _____ cm

= _____ cm

Or:

_____ × _____ cm = _____ cm

2 In these questions the lengths of each side are written in symbols.

You can add them just like numbers. Find the perimeter of each shape.

a

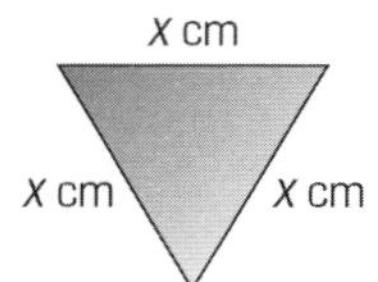

The perimeter is:

____

= _____ cm

Or:

_____ × _____ cm = _____ cm

b

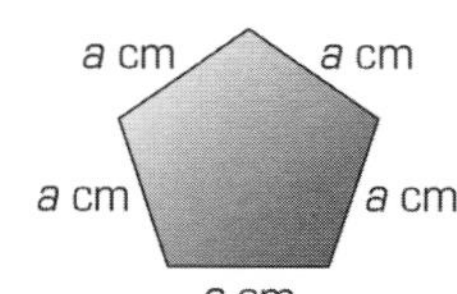

The perimeter is:

____

= _____ cm

Or:

_____ × _____ cm = _____ cm

16b Functions

1 Use the rule in the machine to complete each number mapping.

a

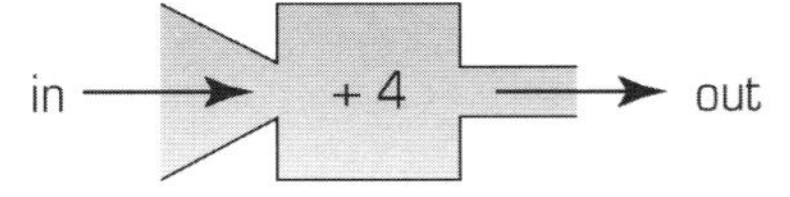

in	→	out
3	→	7
16	→	☐
32	→	☐

b

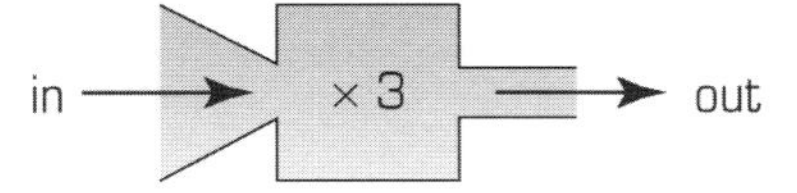

in	→	out
2	→	6
10	→	☐
30	→	☐

c

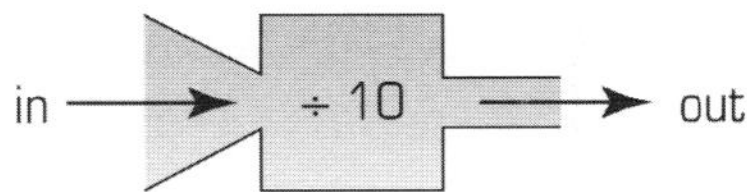

in	→	out
30	→	☐
50	→	☐
120	→	☐

2 For each mapping:

- ► Use pairs of values in the mappings to decide on the rule.
- ► Write the rule into the machine.
- ► Use the rule to complete the mapping.

a

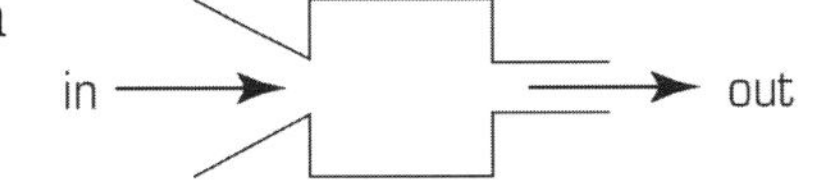

in	→	out
3	→	12
5	→	☐
10	→	40

b

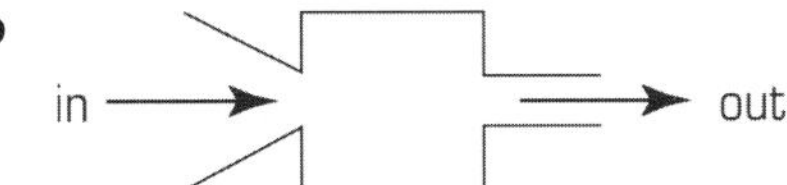

in	→	out
15	→	☐
10	→	6
28	→	24

c

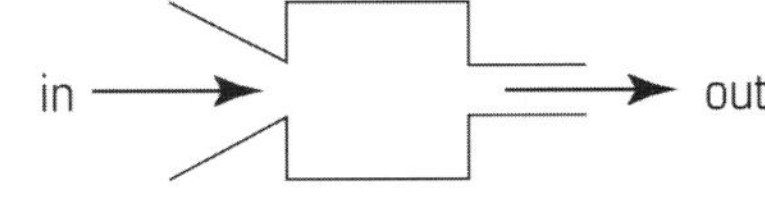

in	→	out
30	→	15
50	→	☐
12	→	6

3 This is the rule that connects the number of white and grey beads in a necklace.

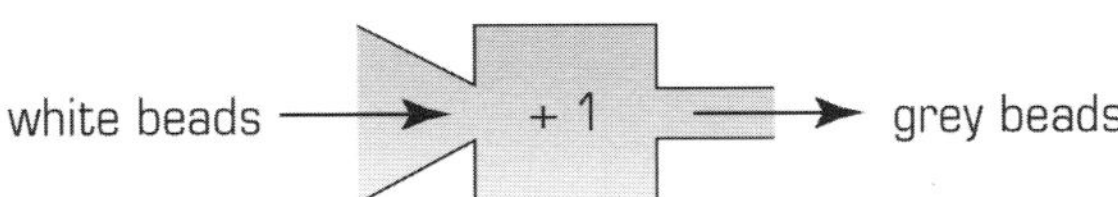

Shade the grey beads on the drawing using the rule.

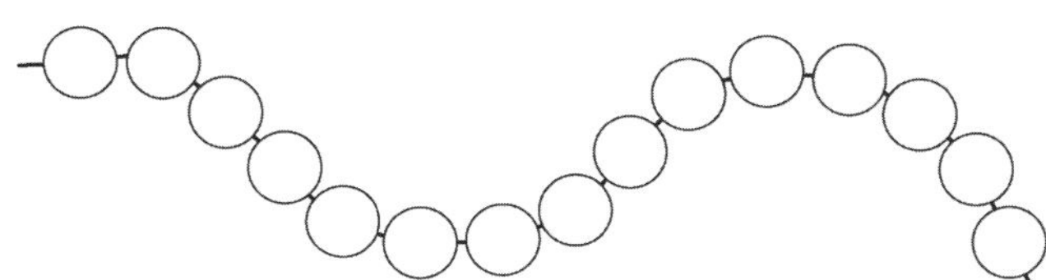

16c Using functions

I can do this page!

1 Mike is paid £3 for every car that he washes.

You can show the formula like this:

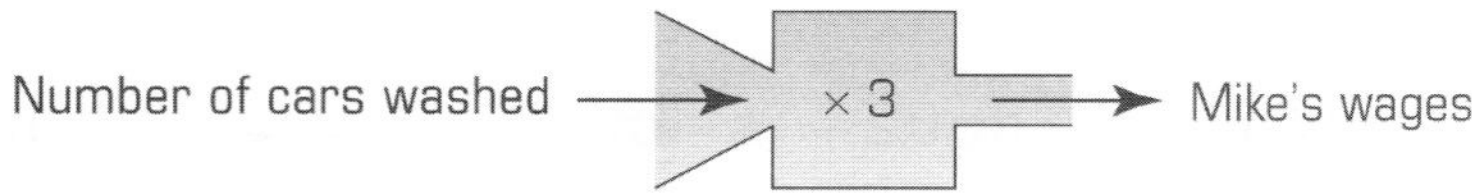

Use the machines to work out Mike's wages for these number of cars washed.

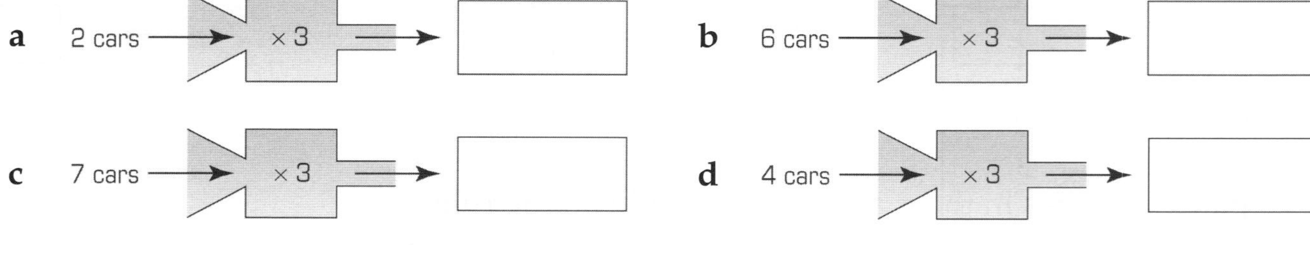

2 Fill in these machines to show Mike's wages when he is paid £5 per car.

a 2 cars → × 5 → ☐　　**b** 4 cars → × 5 → ☐

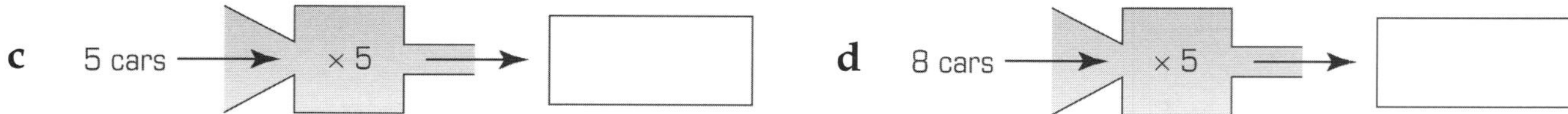

e 10 cars → × 5 → ☐　　**f** 15 cars → × 5 → ☐

g 12 cars → × 5 → ☐　　**h** 20 cars → × 5 → ☐

16d Inverse operations

I can do this page!

1 Fill in the operation that undoes each of these operations.

a
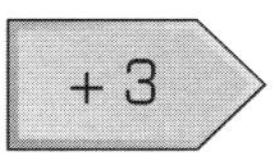

b
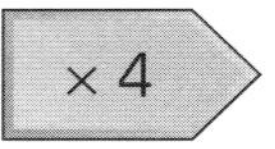

c

d
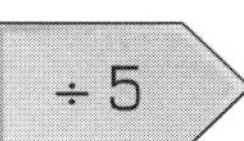

2

F moves a robot forwards.

F3 means go forwards 3 squares.

R means turn right.

L means turn left.

T means turn around.

To move the robot from A to B you write:

F3 – R – F2

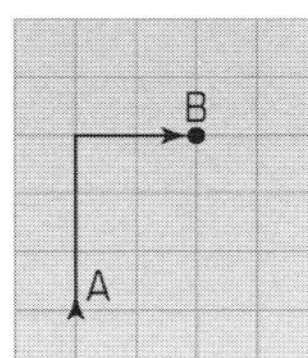

To take the robot back you reverse all the instructions:

T – F2 – L – F3

Draw the path of the robot for:

a F2 – R – F1 – R – F3

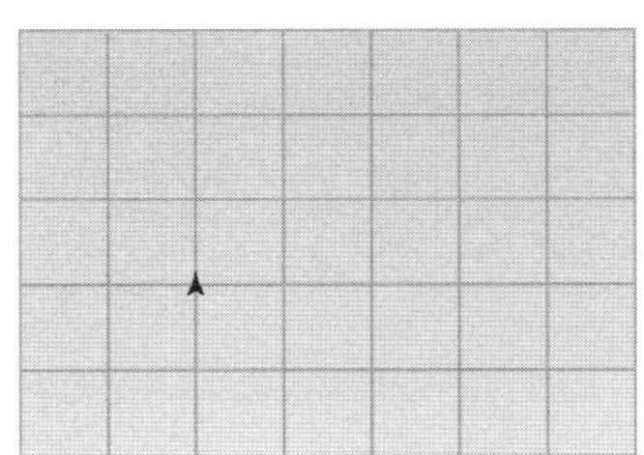

b F1 – L – F3 – R – F2

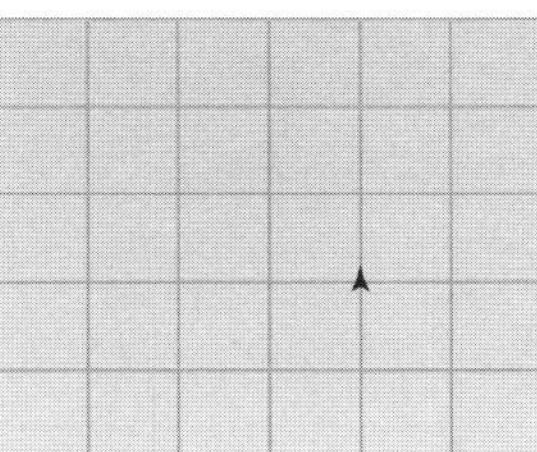

3 For each diagram:

- Give instructions to move the robot from A to B.
- Give the reverse instructions to move the robot back to B.

a

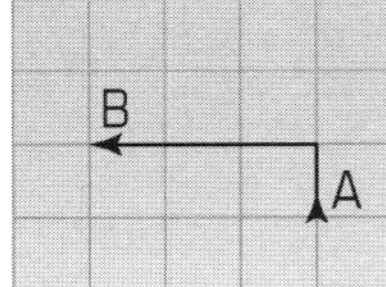

A to B: ______________________

B to A: ______________________

b

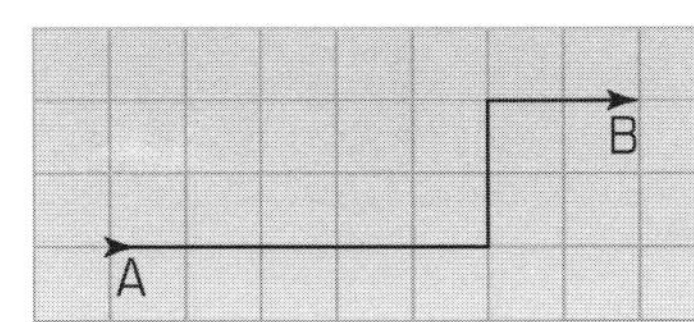

A to B: ______________________

B to A: ______________________

Equations

1 Calculate the weights of the parcels needed to make the scales balance.

Write the weights onto the parcels.

a

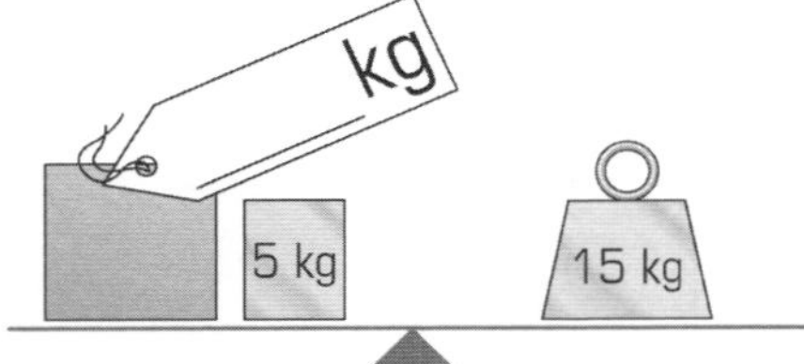

b

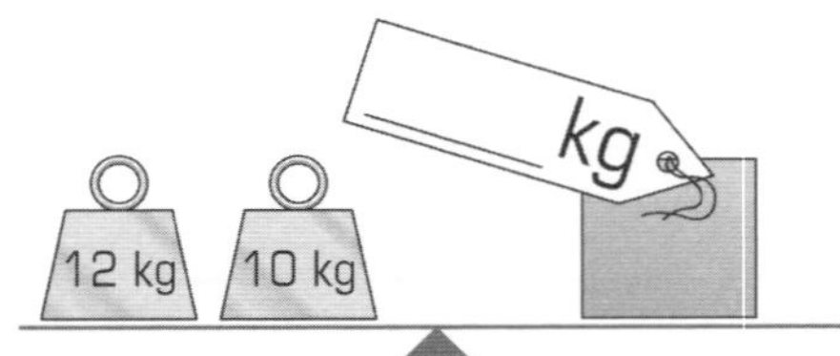

c

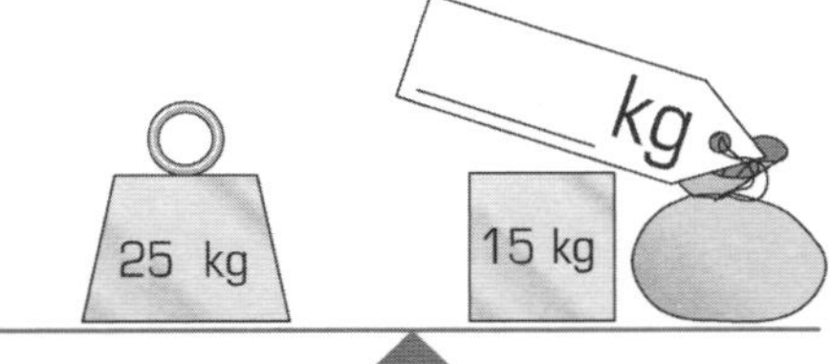

d

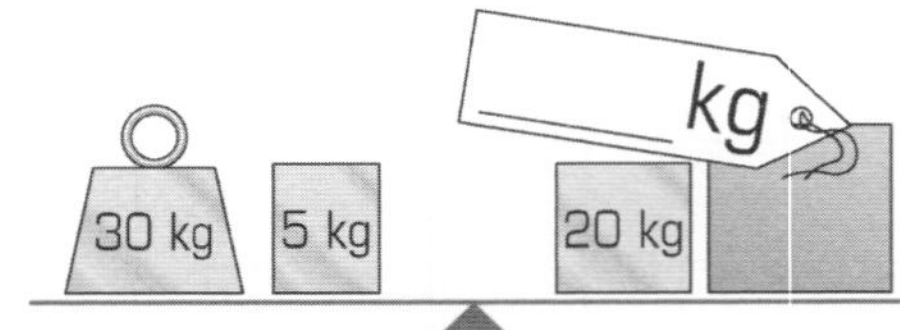

e

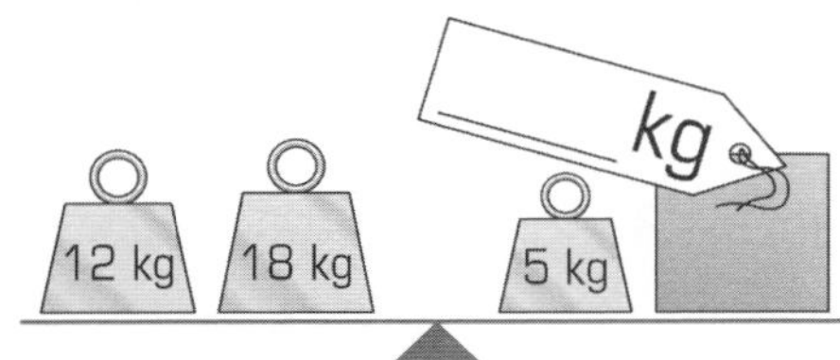

f

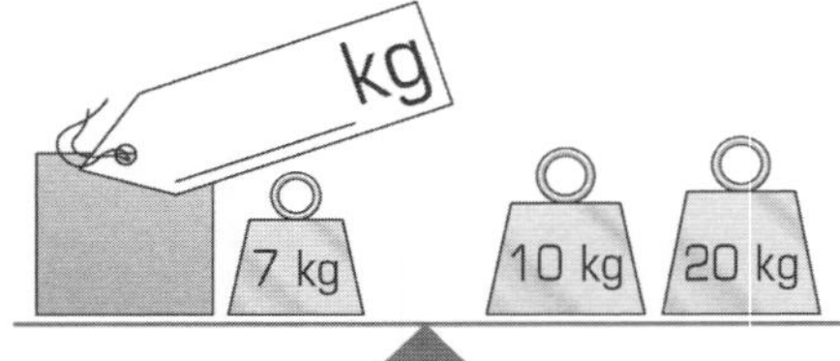

2 Write weights onto this drawing to make these scales balance.

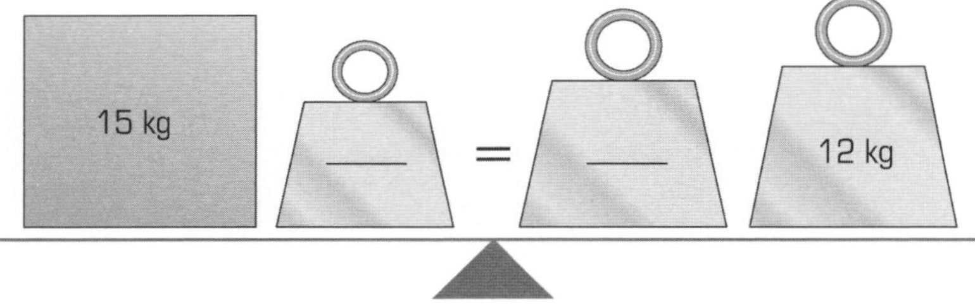

3 Write weights onto these parcels to make the scales balanced.

a

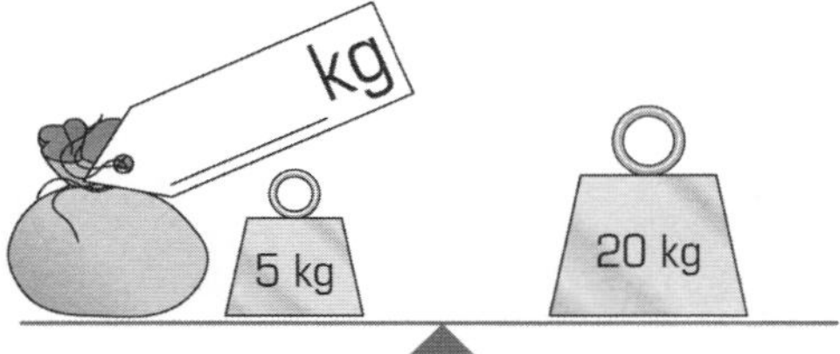

b

16f Using equations

1 Work out the missing weights of the parcels on these scales and write them on.

a

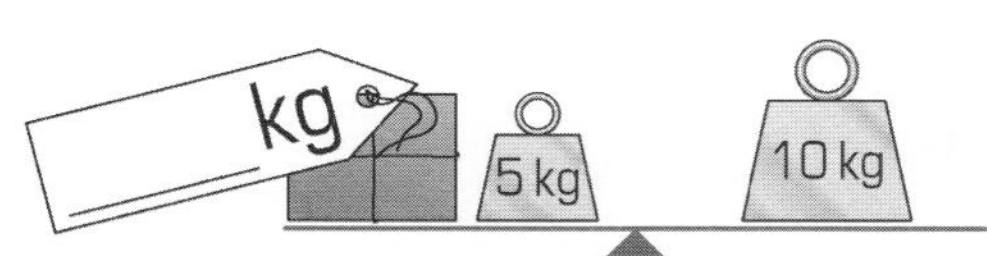

b

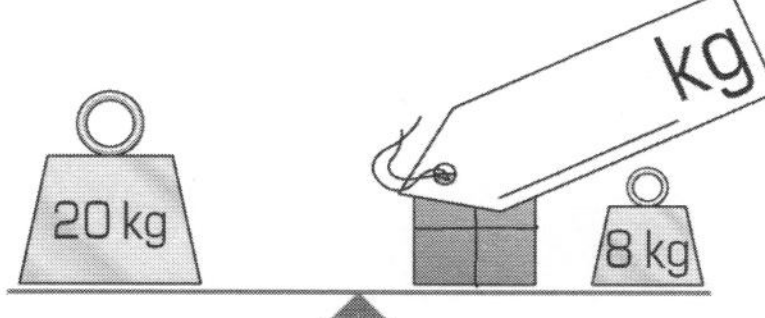

c

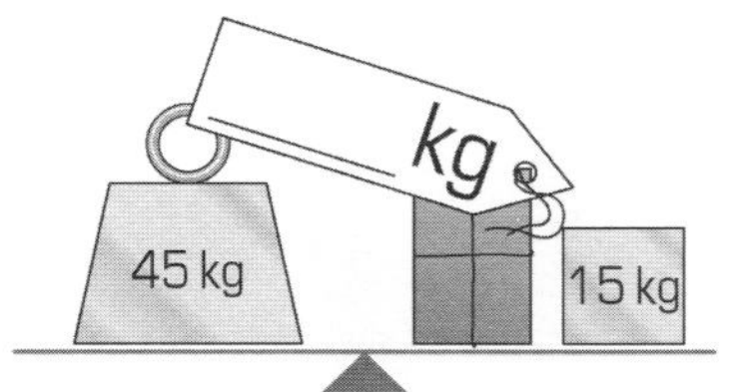

d

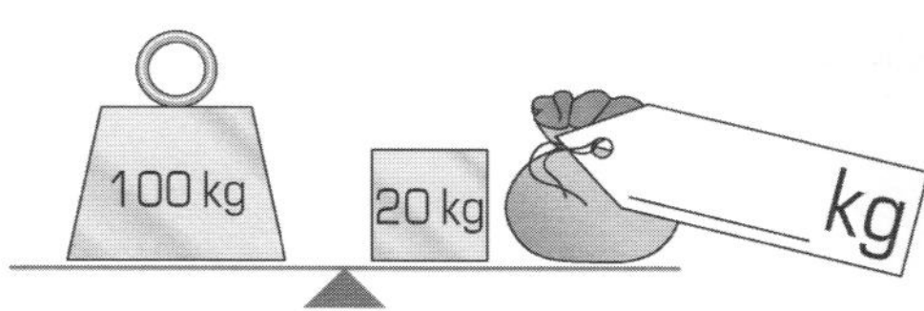

e

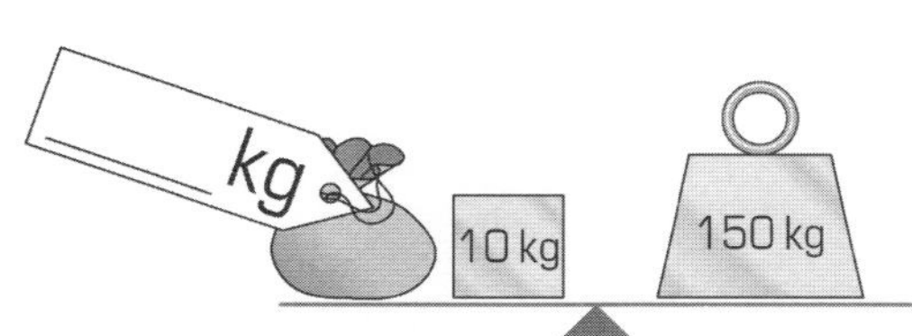

f

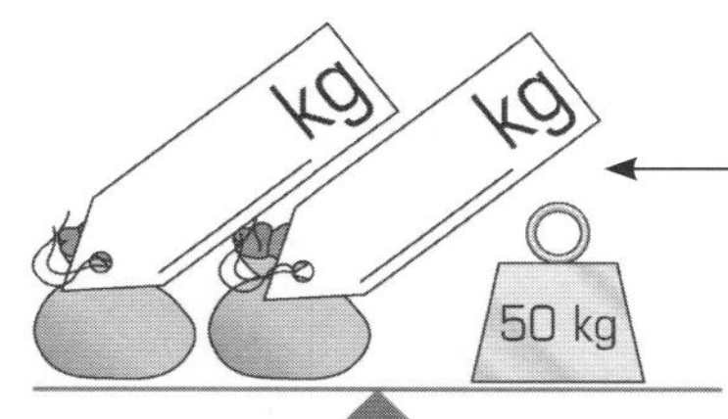

These parcels both weigh the same

2 Use your answers to question **1** to find the value of each letter.

The first one is done for you.

a $a + 5 = 10$

$a = 10 - 5$

$a = 5$

b $b + 8 = 20$

$b = 20 - 8$

$b =$ _____

c $c + 15 = 45$

$c = 45 - 15$

$c =$ _____

d $d + 20 = 80$

$d =$ _____ $-$ _____

$d =$ _____

e $e + 10 = 150$

$e =$ _____ $-$ _____

$e =$ _____

f $2f = 50$

$f = 50 \div 2$

$f =$ _____

Maths Life
Origami
Trace these origami shapes on your page.
Label the shapes you have drawn with names from the list.
I can do this page!
square
rectangle
triangle
pentagon
isosceles
right-angled

17a Calculating angles

1 There are 90° in a right angle.

Calculate the size of the missing angle.

a

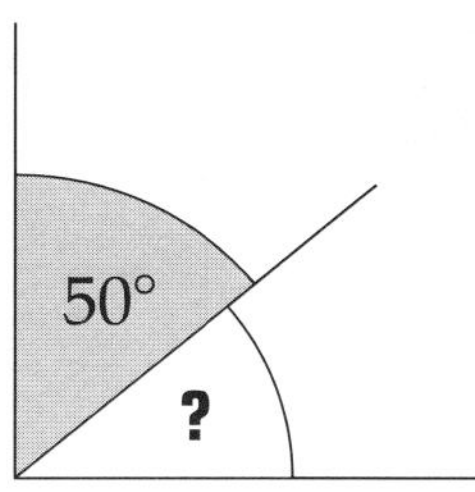

$50 + ? = 90°$

$? =$ ______

b

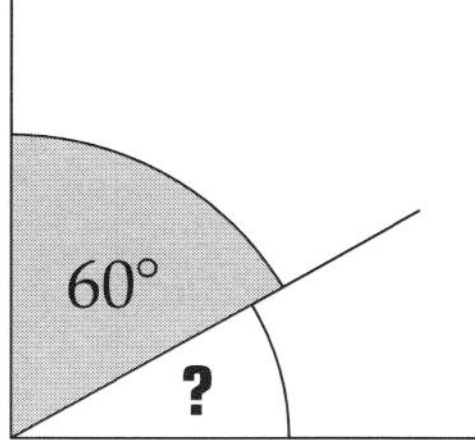

$60° + ? =$ ______

$? =$ ______

c

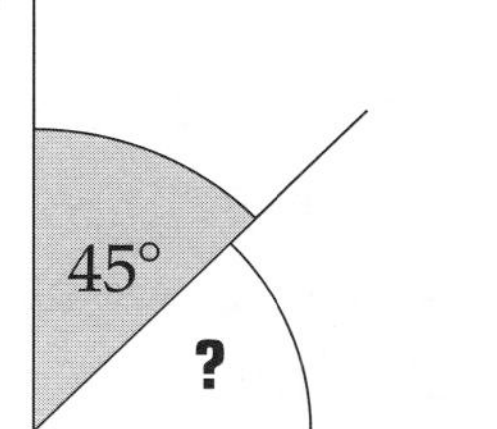

$45° + ? =$ ______

$? =$ ______

2 There are 180° on a straight line.

Calculate the size of the missing angle.

a

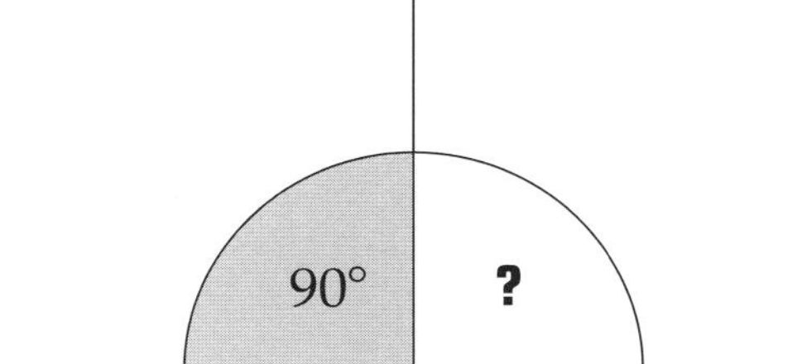

$90° + ? = 180°$

$? =$ ______

b

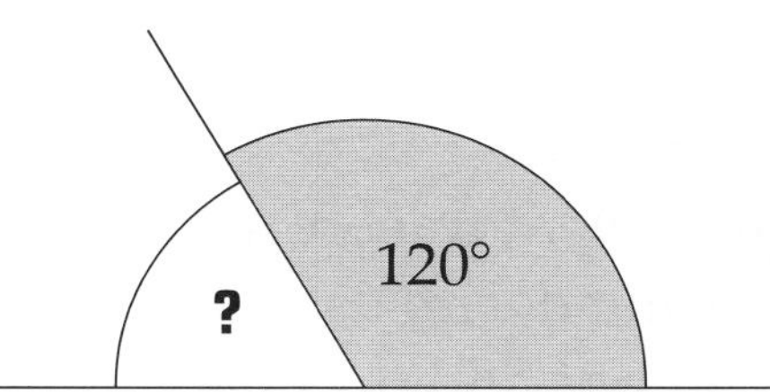

$120° + ? =$ ______

$? =$ ______

c

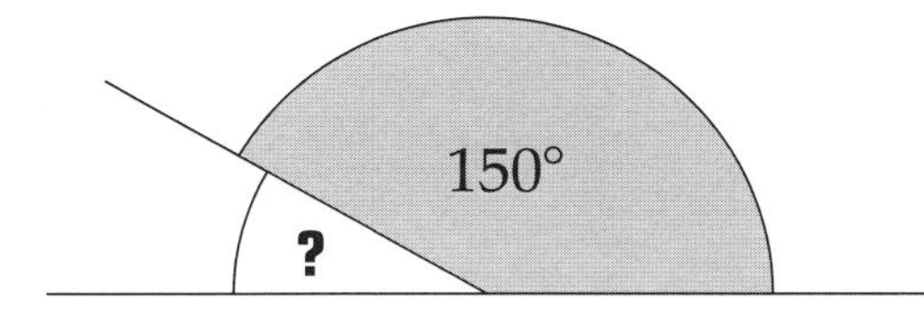

$150° + ? =$ ______

$? =$ ______

Checklist – I can do it!

Page	Title		I can do it!
1	1b	Place value	◯
2	1c	Temperature	◯
3	1d	Mental methods of addition	◯
4	1e	Mental methods of subtraction	◯
5	2a	Sequences	◯
6	2b	Describing sequences	◯
7	2c	Using rules	◯
8	2d	Sequences with negative numbers	◯
9	2e	Functions	◯
10	2f	Mapping	◯
11	3a	Measuring lines	◯
12	3b	Reading scales	◯
13	3c	Time	◯
14	3e	Perimeter	◯
15	3f	Area	◯
16	3g	Angles	◯
17	Case Study – Meet your match		◯
18	4a	Fractions	◯
19	4b	Equivalent fractions	◯
20	4e	Adding decimals	◯
21	4f	Fractions and decimals	◯
22	5a	Data in lists and tables	◯
23	5b	Reading and drawing pictograms	◯
24	5c	Reading and drawing bar charts	◯
25	5f	Reading diagrams	◯
26	6a	Operations	◯
27	6c	Using symbols	◯
28	6d	Substitution	◯
29	7a	Rounding and estimating	◯
30	7b	Mental multiplication	◯
31	7c	Written multiplication	◯
32	7d	Division	◯
33	7e	Division problems	◯
34	7g	Metric units	◯
35	7h	Measuring and accuracy	◯
36	8c	Introducing probability	◯

Multiplication table

×	1	2	3	4	5	6	7	8	9	10
1	1	2	3	4	5	6	7	8	9	10
2	2	4	6	8	10	12	14	16	18	20
3	3	6	9	12	15	18	21	24	27	30
4	4	8	12	16	20	24	28	32	36	40
5	5	10	15	20	25	30	35	40	45	50
6	6	12	18	24	30	36	42	48	54	60
7	7	14	21	28	35	42	49	56	63	70
8	8	16	24	32	40	48	56	64	72	80
9	9	18	27	36	45	54	63	72	81	90
10	10	20	30	40	50	60	70	80	90	100